THE ULTIMATE
DETROIT RED WINGS
TRIVIA BOOK

A Collection of Amazing Trivia Quizzes
and Fun Facts for Die-Hard Red Wings Fans!

Ray Walker

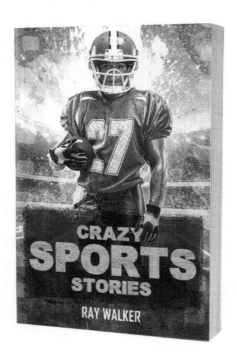

CONTENTS

INTRODUCTION

Detroit Red Wings' fans are certainly among the most vocal, passionate, and loyal fans in the world of sports. They know their hockey and aren't afraid to let their organization know if the team has been underachieving. Fans have been loyally following the club since its inception in the 1920s, and they proudly wear the red-and-white colors of their favorite team.

The team began as the Falcons, became the Cougars, and finally the Red Wings but, whatever the name, fans have excitedly cheered the team on since Day One. The franchise has experienced several lows and numerous highs over the years, but this Original Six team is still the most successful American-based club in the NHL when it comes to Stanley Cup triumphs.

Dozens of Hall of Fame players, coaches and officials have been part of the organization, and 81 of them have already been inducted into the hallowed hall.

This Detroit Red Wings' trivia and fact book celebrates the franchise's history through the conclusion of the 2019-20 regular-season campaign. It's a trip down memory lane for Red Wings' fans and something new for those who may have just discovered the team.

1

Each of the book's 15 chapters serves up a particular topic in Red Wings' history, challenging your status as a knowledgeable fan of the team. Each section offers a combination of 20 multiple-choice and true-or-false questions with the answers on the next page, followed by 10 "Did You Know" facts about the squad.

The book is meant to entertain and educate about the famous Detroit franchise and can also be used to challenge fellow Red Wings supporters to see who the number one fan really is.

There are several excellent reasons to check out the trivia book. Whichever reason you choose, you'll be sure to feel your bond with your favorite NHL team strengthen.

This book will help fill your head with knowledge about the team and will hopefully reaffirm your standing as a certified expert on the Detroit Red Wings.

CHAPTER 1:

ORIGINS & HISTORY

QUIZ TIME!

1. In what year was the Detroit NHL franchise founded?

    a. 1924

    b. 1926

    c. 1923

    d. 1925

2. For how many years did Jack Adams coach the Red Wings?

    a. 17

    b. 19

    c. 18

    d. 20

3. The original name for the franchise was the Detroit Red Wings.

    a. True

    b. False

4. When did Detroit win its first Stanley Cup?

    a. 1934-35

    b. 1936-37

    c. 1935-36

    d. 1932-33

5. Which season did the Red Wings earn a franchise-high 131 points?

    a. 1995-96

    b. 1994-95

    c. 1991-92

    d. 1992-93

6. How many times did Detroit make the playoffs in the team's first 10 seasons?

    a. 8

    b. 5

    c. 7

    d. 6

7. How many wins did the club have in its first season?

    a. 14

    b. 13

    c. 12

    d. 10

8. Detroit played its home games in Windsor, Ontario, in its first NHL season.

    a. True

    b. False

9. How many times has the club appeared in the playoffs since its inception?

    a. 65

    b. 64

    c. 62

    d. 60

10. How many Stanley Cups have the Red Wings won?

    a. 12

    b. 9

    c. 11

    d. 10

11. The Red Wings played in Border Cities Arena until December 1979.

    a. True

    b. False

12. How many members of the Detroit franchise organization have been inducted into the Hockey Hall of Fame?

    a. 68

    b. 63

    c. 77

    d. 81

13. Who did Detroit meet in their first-ever NHL game?

    a. Boston Bruins

    b. New York Rangers

    c. Montreal Maroons

    d. Chicago Black Hawks

14. The Red Wings played 19 seasons in the Western Conference.

    a. True
    b. False

15. How many regular-season points did the Red Wings have when they won their first Stanley Cup?

    a. 60
    b. 48
    c. 56
    d. 55

16. What was the Red Wings' longest streak of consecutive playoff appearances?

    a. 24
    b. 25
    c. 22
    d. 19

17. The Red Wings played their first outdoor game in which venue?

    a. Marquette Branch Prison
    b. College football stadium
    c. Soccer field
    d. Lake Michigan

18. Which aquatic animal is traditionally thrown onto the ice at Red Wings games?

    a. Trout
    b. Squid

c. Lobster

d. Octopus

19. Who did the Red Wings beat to win their second Stanley Cup in 1936-37?

    a. New York Americans

    b. New York Rangers

    c. Toronto Maple Leafs

    d. Chicago Black Hawks

20. Detroit had two coaches in their inaugural season.

    a. True

    b. False

QUIZ ANSWERS

1. B – 1926

2. D – 20

3. B – False

4. C – 1935-36

5. A – 1995-96

6. B – 5

7. C – 12

8. A – True

9. B – 64

10. C – 11

11. B – False

12. C – 77

13. A – Boston Bruins

14. A – True

15. C – 56

16. B – 25

17. A – Marquette Branch Prison

18. D – Octopus

19. B – New York Rangers

20. A – True

DID YOU KNOW?

1. The Detroit Red Wings are based in Detroit, Michigan, and play in the NHL's Atlantic Division in the Eastern Conference. The franchise, originally founded in 1926, is known as one of the league's "Original Six" teams. The club made its NHL debut in 1926-27 as the Detroit Cougars and then became the Detroit Falcons from 1930 to 1932, after which the Red Wings name was adopted.

2. The NHL approved a Detroit franchise in May 1926 for the Townsend-Seyburn group with Charles A. Hughes as its governor. The new franchise bought the players from the Victoria Cougars of the defunct Western Hockey League (WHL) to stock its roster; that's why the Detroit club was originally named the Cougars.

3. The Detroit franchise was bought by James E. Norris in 1932 and he quickly renamed the team the Red Wings. When Norris passed away in 1952, his daughter Marguerite took over as president of the franchise, becoming the first female in NHL history to do so. Her brother Bruce took over in 1955.

4. In 1982, Bruce Norris sold the franchise to Mike Ilitch, who was the founder of the Little Caesars pizza restaurant chain. Ilitch passed away in February 2017 and his son Christopher took over the Ilitch holdings business. Mike Ilitch, who also owned the Detroit Tigers MLB franchise, was inducted into the Hockey Hall of Fame in 2003.

5. Detroit has won 11 Stanley Cups, which is the most by an American-based NHL squad and third overall in the league behind the Montreal Canadiens and Toronto Maple Leafs. Their first Cup victory came in 1935-36 and the last one was celebrated in 2007-08. Their minor-league affiliates are the Grand Rapids Griffins of the American Hockey League (AHL) and the Toledo Walleye of the East Coast Hockey League (ECHL).

6. The franchise played its first season in Windsor, Canada, before moving to Olympia Stadium in Detroit for the next 52 years. The team then moved to the newly-built Joe Louis Arena in December 1979 and stayed there until 2017. The club then moved again when Little Caesars Arena was opened in downtown Detroit.

7. Between the 1931-32 and 1965-66 seasons, Detroit failed to make the postseason just four times. However, the team's fortunes changed as the Red Wings made the playoffs just twice between 1966-67 and 1982-83. They rebounded and made the postseason in 30 of 32 seasons between 1983-84 and 2015-16.

8. The franchise set a North American pro sports record by making the playoffs 25 seasons in a row between 1990-91 and 2015-16, excluding the 2004-05 NHL season, which was canceled. The quarter-century run of making the postseason tied the third-longest streak in the history of the NHL.

9. The name Jack Adams was well known by the team's fans

beginning in 1927-28 because he coached the team that season and for the following 36 years he was either the head coach or general manager. The NHL's award for the best coach of the regular-season is named after Adams.

10. It's generally considered that the Red Wings experienced two NHL dynasties as the league's dominant club. They won the Stanley Cup four times between 1947 and 1956 when the great Gordie Howe was with the team. In addition, they captured the Cup another three times between 1995 and 2002 as well as three conference titles and three President's trophies as the team with the best regular-season record.

CHAPTER 2:

JERSEYS & NUMBERS

QUIZ TIME!

1. How many jersey numbers have the Red Wings retired?

    a. 6
    b. 9
    c. 7
    d. 8

2. The Red Wings logo is commonly referred to as the "winged wheel."

    a. True
    b. False

3. What year were names put on the backs of Red Wings jerseys?

    a. 1972
    b. 1971
    c. 1975
    d. 1974

4. How many alternate Red Wings jerseys have been made for special events?

    a. 6

    b. 5

    c. 3

    d. 4

5. What was the first number retired by the Red Wings?

    a. 10

    b. 7

    c. 9

    d. 1

6. What is unique about the jerseys worn by Detroit from 1930 to 1932?

    a. There were two logos on the front

    b. The numbers were on the front

    c. They featured a cougar as the logo

    d. It was the only time a third color was used

7. Which number has been worn by 61 players in Detroit since 1951?

    a. 58

    b. 84

    c. 21

    d. 10

8. The Red Wings jersey has remained the same since 1987.

    a. True

    b. False

9. Who wore number 50 from 2013 to 2015?

    a. Carlo Colaiacovo
    b. Jonas Gustavsson
    c. Thomas McCollum
    d. Ryan Sproul

10. How many Red Wings have worn number 18 since 1951?

    a. 18
    b. 42
    c. 30
    d. 56

11. The Red Wings have never worn an alternate jersey for an entire regular season.

    a. True
    b. False

12. Which number did Terry Sawchuk not wear as a member of the Red Wings?

    a. 1
    b. 30
    c. 45
    d. 29

13. Who was the first player to wear number 2 for the team?

    a. Clare Martin
    b. Clem Loughlin
    c. Lefty Wilson
    d. Benny Woit

14. The Red Wings had only one jersey color for their first 13 seasons.

    a. True
    b. False

15. Which number did Gordie Howe wear before switching to number 9?

    a. 17
    b. 19
    c. 7
    d. 10

16. Which number has not been worn by a Red Wing?

    a. 59
    b. 84
    c. 23
    d. 75

17. Which player wore number 11 from 2006 to 2015 with a one-season gap in 2013-14?

    a. Dan Cleary
    b. Riley Sheahan
    c. Brendan Smith
    d. Joakim Andersson

18. Who was the last player to wear number 1 for the Red Wings?

    a. Filip Zadina
    b. Glen Hanlon
    c. Eric Comrie
    d. Calvin Pickard

19. The Red Wings have used the letter D styled in old English font on three jerseys.

   a. True
   b. False

20. Pavel Datsyuk wore this number for 14 years in Detroit.

   a. 12
   b. 11
   c. 13
   d. 14

QUIZ ANSWERS

1. D – 8

2. A – True

3. A – 1972

4. B – 5

5. C – 9

6. D – It was the only time a third color was used

7. C – 21

8. A – True

9. B – Jonas Gustavsson

10. D – 56

11. A – True

12. C – 45

13. B – Clem Loughlin

14. B – False

15. A – 17

16. D – 75

17. A – Dan Cleary

18. C – Eric Comrie

19. B – False

20. C – 13

DID YOU KNOW?

1. The Red Wings' jerseys are predominantly red with white trimming or predominantly white with red trimming and haven't significantly changed since the 1930s. The word Detroit was replaced by the team's current logo in 1932, when the team's name was changed from the Falcons to the Red Wings.

2. When James Norris bought the franchise in 1932, he brought the logo of the Montreal Amateur Athletic Association with him. This featured a winged wheel that was originally designed for cycling. Norris believed a red version of the winged wheel was ideal for a club that played in Detroit, which was nicknamed "Motor City." That's how the Red Wings' famous logo was born.

3. The Red Wings' winged wheel logo was voted the second best in the NHL by The Hockey News in 2008. The league's best logo was considered to be that of the Chicago Blackhawks. The Red Wings have used alternate or one-time-only jerseys and-or logos only a few times throughout the team's history.

4. Eight different jersey numbers have been retired by the Red Wings and all eight players are members of the Hockey Hall of Fame. Those with retired numbers are Terry Sawchuk (1), Red Kelly (4), Nicklas Lidström (5), Ted Lindsay (7), Gordie Howe (9), Alex Delvecchio (10), Sid Abel (12) and Steve Yzerman (19).

5. Even though the numbers 7 and 16 haven't officially been retired by the franchise, no player is issued them anymore. Number 6 was worn by Larry Aurie while Vladimir Konstantinov was the last to wear 16. Number 6 was retired in 1938 but current ownership doesn't consider it to be retired; it was worn by Cummy Burton in 1958-59. Nobody has worn number 16 since Konstantinov was disabled in a 1997 automobile accident.

6. Number 91 hasn't been retired by Detroit either but no player has worn the jersey since Hall-of-Famer Sergei Fedorov left the team. The Russian center joined the squad in 1990-91 and wore the sweater for 13 seasons before signing as an unrestricted free agent with Anaheim in 2003.

7. The most popular jersey in Detroit history has been the number 21. A total of 71 players have worn the sweater. Among them are Andre Pronovost, Andy Bathgate, Pete Mahovlich, Ron Stackhouse and Danny Grant, and Hall-of-Famers Marcel Pronovost, Adam Oates and Börje Salming.

8. The lowest jersey number worn by Red Wings' players is number 1, which was worn by many of the team's goaltenders. The highest number donned by a player is number 96, which belonged to Tomas Holmström between 1998 and 2012.

9. Every jersey number between 1 and 57 has been worn by at least one Red Wing. In addition, 21 numbers between 59 and 96 have been worn at least once.

10. It appears that Red Wing players may be a bit more superstitious than others because just three players have worn number 13 in club history. However, the last two to wear the number did so for numerous years. Vyacheslav Kozlov donned the sweater between 1992 and 2001 while Pavel Datsyuk took it over from 2002 to 2016.

CHAPTER 3:

FAMOUS QUOTES

QUIZ TIME!

1. Which Red Wing said, "All pro athletes are bilingual. They speak English and profanity"?

    a. Mike Foligno

    b. Wendel Clark

    c. Gordie Howe

    d. Dylan Larkin

2. "Dirty isn't a derogatory word. It's a good thing to be called in hockey." Steve Yzerman said this about which player?

    a. Dale Hunter

    b. Chris Simon

    c. Chris Nilan

    d. Basil McRae

3. Former Red Wing Marcel Dionne said, "Statistics are for losers, unless you have good ones."

    a. True

    b. False

4. Which former Red Wing said this about former coach Mike Keenan: "He's the kind of guy that will stab you in the back to your face"?

    a. Brett Hull
    b. Adam Oates
    c. Chris Chelios
    d. Paul Coffey

5. "A hockey player without a stick is like a duck without wings," was said by which Red Wing?

    a. Mike Blaisdell
    b. Joey Kocur
    c. Todd Bertuzzi
    d. Mickey Redmond

6. "Every boo on the road is a cheer," was claimed by which Detroit head coach?

    a. Jeff Blashill
    b. Bill Gadsby
    c. Scotty Bowman
    d. Brad Park

7. Which Red Wing was general manager Steve Yzerman referring to when he said in 2019-20, "You claim him off waivers, so it's just a dollar figure."

    a. Tyler Bertuzzi
    b. Robby Fabbri
    c. Dmytro Timashov
    d. Gustav Lindström

8. Enforcer Bob Probert once said he was thinking of quitting hockey to become a professional boxer.

   a. True
   b. False

1. Which veteran Red Wing said, "By 1946, I knew Detroit was the best hockey city in the Original Six"?

   a. Ted Lindsay
   b. Red Kelly
   c. Terry Sawchuk
   d. Syd Howe

2. When talking about high school hockey, which Red Wing claimed, "I tried out for the 'A' team and I was cut after one practice"?

   a. Nicklas Lidström
   b. Joey Kocur
   c. Paul Henderson
   d. Red Kelly

3. Detroit goaltender Terry Sawchuk said, "The day they put me in net, I had a good game. I've stayed there ever since."

   a. True
   b. False

4. "I really hope that I set a good path for kids coming up and playing hockey in Detroit," was said by which player?

   a. Anthony Mantha
   b. Dylan Larkin
   c. Jimmy Howard
   d. Roger Crozier

5. Which Detroit goaltender claimed, "Only Dunlop has seen more rubber than I have"?

   a. Glenn Hall
   b. Glen Hanlon
   c. Jonathan Bernier
   d. Dominik Hasek

6. Mickey Redmond came up with this famous quote, "Half the game of hockey is mental and the other half is being mental."

   a. True
   b. False

7. This quote was attributed to which Red Wing, "Sometimes guys need to cry. Some hockey players think they're too tough to cry"?

   a. Bob Probert
   b. Murray Craven
   c. Brett Hull
   d. Mike Foligno

8. Who once claimed, "If someone gave the Russians a football they'd win the Super Bowl within two years"?

   a. Pete Mahovlich
   b. Frank Mahovlich
   c. Gary Bergman
   d. Norm Ullman

9. Which Red Wings' coach was general manager Sid Abel talking about when he said, "I don't know how to evaluate him as a coach because I don't think he is one"?

a. Ned Harkness

b. Bill Gadsby

c. Johnny Wilson

d. Ted Garvin

10. Which member of the Red Wings said, "You go through bumps in the road and you see who your true fans and best friends are"?

a. Tyler Bertuzzi

b. Todd Bertuzzi

c. Nicklas Kronwall

d. Kirk Maltby

11. "You go to the net and good things happen...sometimes." This was a quote by which Red Wings' high-scoring forward?

a. Pavel Datsyuk

b. Sergei Fedorov

c. Steve Yzerman

d. John Ogrodnick

12. After signing as a free agent with Detroit, Börje Salming remarked, "I just met my new teammates and trainers and I'm sure I'm going to have to ask their names again tomorrow."

a. True

b. False

QUIZ ANSWERS

1. C – Gordie Howe

2. A – Dale Hunter

3. B – False

4. A – Brett Hull

5. D – Mickey Redmond

6. C – Scotty Bowman

7. C – Dmytro Timashov

8. B – False

9. A – Ted Lindsay

10. D – Red Kelly

11. A – True

12. B – Dylan Larkin

13. D – Dominik Hasek

14. B – False

15. C – Brett Hull

16. B – Frank Mahovlich

17. A – Ned Harkness

18. B – Todd Bertuzzi

19. B – Sergei Fedorov

20. B – False

DID YOU KNOW?

1. Hall-of-Famer Ted Lindsay was quoted as saying, "I had the idea that I should beat up every player I tangled with and nothing ever convinced me it wasn't a good idea." Lindsay served 1,423 minutes in penalties in 862 regular-season games with Detroit and another 179 minutes in 123 playoff contests.

2. After Ted Lindsay passed away in 2019, former Detroit general manager Ken Holland said, "Ted was the most fearless hockey player of all-time, but his skill level could match any player from his era. He was always a regular visitor to the Red Wings dressing room, and there was never a single player who didn't go out of their way to introduce themselves and come away awed by the experience."

3. "I like fun and I like Rambo. I like music. I like cars and I like pizza." This was what forward Petr Klíma told the press when he came to Detroit to play for the club and owner Mike Ilitch, the founder of Little Caesars Pizza. Klíma also remarked, "I have one goal in each stick," when asked why he breaks his stick every time he scored a goal.

4. When Gordie Howe was a guest on the Dick Cavett television talk show in the 1970s, Cavett asked him why hockey players wore a protective cup but hardly any of them wore a helmet. Howe replied, "You can always get someone to do your thinking for you."

5. Hall of Fame blue-liner and former Red Wings captain Nicklas Lidström explained why the team had been so successful in the postseason by remarking, "You have to pay attention to details to have success in the playoffs. You can't take anyone lightly."

6. When talking about doing anything to help the team, another Detroit captain and Hall-of-Famer, Steve Yzerman, commented, "I feel I adapted. I was willing to try to fit into any role. The way I figured, it was always up to me to prove my worth, that I deserved to be here."

7. When the Red Wings entered the 2015-16 playoffs, head coach Mike Babcock told the media, "I like our team. I like our opportunity. Every year, there's 16 teams right now who think they have a chance. I've been through it enough, you have the chance to win the Cup after you win 15 games. We've won no games in the playoffs so we're just gonna keep trying to get better."

8. On the television show Scrubs, which originally ran from 2001 to 2009, the Dr. Cox character once remarked, "For the next twenty minutes, you will sit in silence while I tell you why the Detroit Red Wings are the greatest franchise in the history of professional sports."

9. Red Wings' television broadcaster and former player Mickey Redmond is well known for his colorful quotes. During a Wings-Toronto Maple Leafs game in 1997, he said, "Detroit's had some chances. They haven't been able to extend their lead and Toronto's just hanging around there like a bad smell right now."

10. Scotty Bowman, former head coach of the Red Wings, appeared to have a love-hate relationship with his players. Some loved him but many hated him. Bowman once said, "I don't have bad relationships with my players. But I don't get into long conversations with them either."

CHAPTER 4:

CATCHY NICKNAMES

QUIZ TIME!

1. Which shifty Detroit forward was nicknamed "Magic Man"?

   a. Pavel Datsyuk

   b. Danny Grant

   c. Nick Libett

   d. Dale McCourt

2. This Red Wings' defenseman was known as "The King."

   a. Nicklas Lidström

   b. Börje Salming

   c. John Barrett

   d. Doug Barkley

3. "Radar" was the moniker given to this Red Wing.

   a. Al Arbour

   b. Andy Bathgate

   c. Thommie Bergman

   d. Leo Boivin

4. This Detroit winger was known as "Spud."

    a. Errol Thompson
    b. Jeff Brubaker
    c. Damien Brunner
    d. Erik Cole

5. Dan Maloney's nickname was?

    a. Rocketman
    b. Snowshoes
    c. Baloney
    d. Danny Boy

6. Brett Hull was known as "The Golden Jet."

    a. True
    b. False

7. Red Kelly's real first name was?

    a. Leonard
    b. Steven
    c. Barry
    d. Randy

8. Who was known as "The Big M"?

    a. Frank Mahovlich
    b. Pete Mahovlich
    c. Mike Commodore
    d. Murray Eaves

9. Who was known as "The Little M"?

    a. Frank Mahovlich
    b. Gerry Ehman

   c. Mark Major

   d. Pete Mahovlich

10. The given name of Mud Bruneteau is?

   a. Modere Fernand

   b. Muff

   c. Martin

   d. Michael

11. Ted Lindsay's nickname was simply "Terrible Ted."

   a. True

   b. False

12. "Little Ball of Hate" was the nickname given to which Red Wing?

   a. Tony McKegney

   b. Kris King

   c. Murray Costello

   d. Pat Verbeek

13. Berry Melrose was referred to as "The Mullet Man."

   a. True

   b. False

14. Winger John McKenzie was known as "Pie Face."

   a. True

   b. False

15. What was Vladimir Konstantinov's nickname?

   a. Vlad the Impaler

   b. The Vladiator

c. The Flying V

d. Konny

16. Enforcers Bob Probert and Joey Kocur were collectively known as "The Bruise Brothers."

    a. True

    b. False

17. This Red Wing was affectionately known as "The Professor."

    a. Henrik Zetterberg

    b. Danny Markov

    c. Sergei Fedorov

    d. Igor Larionov

18. What animal nickname did Gustav Nyquist have?

    a. Goose

    b. Gander

    c. The Owl

    d. The Eagle

19. One of this player's nicknames was "The Perfect Human."

    a. Chris Chelios

    b. Nicklas Lidström

    c. Ebbie Goodfellow

    d. Doug Harvey

20. Which Hall-of-Famer was nicknamed "The Little Beaver"?

    a. Sid Abel

    b. Václav Nedomanský

    c. Paul Coffey

    d. Marcel Dionne

QUIZ ANSWERS

1. A – Pavel Datsyuk

2. B – Börje Salming

3. A – Al Arbour

4. Errol Thompson

5. B – Snowshoes

6. B – False

7. A – Leonard

8. A – Frank Mahovlich

9. D – Pete Mahovlich

10. A – Modere Fernand

11. A -True

12. D – Pat Verbeek

13. B - False

14. B - False

15. B – The Vladiator

16. A -True

17. D – Igor Larionov

18. A - Goose

19. B– Nicklas Lidström

20. D – Marcel Dionne

DID YOU KNOW?

1. The Red Wing team doesn't really have a nickname but opponents often refer to the squad as "The Dead Things" or "The Dead Wings." This was especially true from 1967 to 1983, when the club made the playoffs just twice.

2. The city of Detroit has been nicknamed "Motor City" and "Motown" over the years but hockey fans and broadcasters have given it the moniker "Hockeytown." In fact, the franchise filed to trademark the Hockeytown name in 1995.

3. The great Gordie Howe was generally known by the nickname "Mr. Hockey" but opponents often called him "Mr. Elbows" because Howe was known to punish players with his high elbows if they got too close to him. In addition, a "Gordie Howe hat trick" is the name given to the feat of a player registering a goal, an assist and a fight in the same game.

4. The famous Red Wings' forward line of right-winger Gordie Howe, left-winger Ted Lindsay and center Sid Abel was known as "The Production Line." All three are enshrined in the Hockey Hall of Fame. In 1949-50, Lindsay led the NHL in scoring with 78 points while Abel finished second with 69 and Howe placed third at 68.

5. The "Russian Five" was the moniker given to five of Detroit's Russian stars in the 1990s. This quintet consisted of centers Sergei Fedorov and Igor Larionov, defensemen

Vladimir Konstantinov and Slava Fetisov, and winger Slava Kozlov. They often played together after head coach Scotty Bowman moved Larionov to the wing. Konstantinov was seriously injured in a car crash after the team won the Stanley Cup in 1997 and never played again.

6. Hall of Fame center Alex Delvecchio was affectionately known as "Fats" by his Detroit teammates. It was due to his chubby face when he broke into the NHL rather than the shape of his body.

7. Forward Tomas Tatar had a few different nicknames while with the Red Wings. He was known as "Souse," "Hot Sauce" and "Sauce." Tatar, who has since left Detroit, is now typically referred to as "Tuna."

8. Steve Yzerman nicknamed winger Johan Franzen "The Mule" because he was impressed that Franzen did absolutely anything he could to help his team succeed. According to Yzerman, Franzen was "The Mule" because he always carried the load when he played.

9. Goaltender Chris Osgood was simply called Oz or Ozzie by some teammates. However, the more creative ones referred to the fan favorite as "The Wizard of Oz" during his playing days in Hockeytown.

10. Another Red Wing goaltender, Curtis Joseph, was known as Cujo. This combines the first two letters of his first and last names. Of course, it was also the name of the large dog in the Stephen King horror movie, Cujo. In fact, Joseph's goalie mask was adorned with the vicious dog's teeth during most of his NHL career.

CHAPTER 5:

THE CAPTAIN CLASS

QUIZ TIME!

1. The Red Wings tried seven different captains in 1973-74.

   a. True
   b. False

2. Who was the longest-serving captain in Detroit hockey history?

   a. Nicklas Lidström
   b. Gordie Howe
   c. Alex Delvecchio
   d. Steve Yzerman

3. Which of the following was never a Red Wing captain?

   a. Dan Maloney
   b. Errol Thompson
   c. Börje Salming
   d. Danny Grant

4. This blue-liner was captain of the 1981-82 squad.

a. Garry Bergman

b. Larry Johnston

c. Terry Harper

d. Reed Larson

5. This former Detroit captain once scored 6 goals in a game.

a. Gordie Howe

b. Mickey Redmond

c. Red Berenson

d. Henrik Zetterberg

6. Mark Howe, Gordie Howe and Syd Howe all captained the Red Wings at one point in their careers.

a. True

b. False

7. In which year was Steve Yzerman named team captain?

a. 1984

b. 1986

c. 1988

d. 1989

8. Brett Hull was one of Detroit's captains.

a. True

b. False

9. Which former Detroit captain was a first overall NHL draft pick?

a. Marcel Dionne

b. Dale McCourt

c. Nicklas Lidström

d. Henrik Zetterberg

10. Who was the first captain in Detroit franchise history?

a. Reg Noble

b. Larry Aurie

c. Art Duncan

d. Flash Hollett

11. Which Detroit captain belongs to a famous hockey family?

a. Red Kelly

b. Herbie Lewis

c. Doug Young

d. Dennis Hextall

12. The Red Wings went without a captain for the 2019-20 season.

a. True

b. False

13. Which Detroit captain was traded to the Los Angeles Kings?

a. Dale McCourt

b. Marcel Dionne

c. Ted Harris

d. Paul Woods

14. This one-time Red Wings' skipper served 274 penalty minutes in the 1976-77 season.

a. Dennis Polonich

b. Danny Grant

c. Dan Maloney

d. Terry Harper

15. This Detroit captain played both defense and forward during his NHL career.

   a. Reed Larson

   b. Gary Bergman

   c. Red Kelly

   d. Carson Cooper

16. Just three former Detroit captains have been inducted into the Hockey Hall of Fame.

   a. True

   b. False

17. Which Red Wing captain was acquired in a trade with the Buffalo Sabres?

   a. Paul Woods

   b. Dale McCourt

   c. Errol Thompson

   d. Danny Gare

18. Who did Ebbie Goodfellow share the Detroit captaincy with in 1941-42?

   a. Sid Abel

   b. Syd Howe

   c. Ted Lindsay

   d. Flash Hollett

19. Which of these Red Wing captains was the franchise's first player to score 50 goals in a season?

a. Gordie Howe

b. Mickey Redmond

c. Ted Lindsay

d. Steve Yzerman

20. How many seasons did Nicklas Lidström wear the "C" on his sweater in Detroit?

a. 3

b. 4

c. 6

d. 2

QUIZ ANSWERS

1. A - True

2. D – Steve Yzerman

3. C – Börje Salming

4. D – Reed Larson

5. C – Red Berenson

6. B – False

7. B – 1986

8. B - False

9. B – Dale McCourt

10. C – Art Duncan

11. D – Dennis Hextall

12. A - True

13. B – Marcel Dionne

14. A – Dennis Polonich

15. C – Red Kelly

16. B - False

17. D – Danny Gare

18. B – Syd Howe

19. B – Mickey Redmond

20. C – 6

DID YOU KNOW?

1. Three dozen different Red Wings have worn the "C" on their sweater in franchise history. The organization had more than one captain in a season several times in its history. In 1973-74 Detroit experimented with a rotating captain system in which seven different players shared the duties.

2. The Red Wings went without a captain in the 2018-19 and 2019-20 seasons, using four alternate captains instead. The club's previous skipper was Henrik Zetterberg, who had held the position since 2013. They haven't named a captain, though, since he retired following the 2017-18 campaign.

3. The first captain of the Red Wings' era was Larry Aurie in 1932-33. The longest-serving captain in the team's history was Hall of Fame center and current general manager Steve Yzerman. He was named captain at the age of 21 in 1986 and held the position until retiring in 2006. Yzerman holds the record as the longest-serving captain in the annals of North American pro sports.

4. Former franchise captains Herbie Lewis, Reg Noble, George Hay, Ebbie Goodfellow, Syd Howe, Sid Abel, Ted Lindsay, Red Kelly, Gordie Howe, Alex Delvecchio, Marcel Dionne, Steve Yzerman and Nicklas Lidström were all inducted into the Hockey Hall of Fame.

5. Before Yzerman, the youngest Red Wing captain was Paul Woods, who was claimed by Detroit from Montreal in the 1977 NHL Waiver Draft. He then played his entire big-league career with the club. In 1979-80, Woods co-captained the team with Dennis Hextall and Nick Libett. He later worked as a radio broadcaster for Red Wings' games.

6. Larry Aurie wore the "C" for Detroit in 1932-33, when the team was renamed the Red Wings. He had joined the club in 1927-28 and spent his entire NHL career in Detroit until he retired following the 1937-38 season. Aurie won a pair of Stanley Cups, and owner James Norris claimed he was the heart and soul of the squad.

7. Ebbie Goodfellow had two stints as Detroit captain. He donned the "C" in 1934-35 and again between 1938 and 1941. Then, in 1941-42, he shared the captaincy with fellow Hall-of-Famer Syd Howe. Goodfellow played all 14 of his NHL seasons with Detroit from 1929 to 1944. He played forward and defense and won three Stanley Cups. He was also the first Red Wing to capture the Hart Trophy as the league's top performer in 1939-40.

8. Syd was the first Howe to captain the Red Wings. The winger shared the duties with Ebbie Goodfellow in 1941-42. Howe played a dozen years with Detroit until 1945-46 and helped the team win three Stanley Cups. Howe tallied 188 goals and 436 points for the franchise in 515 regular-season outings and was inducted into the Hall of Fame in 1965.

9. The most famous Howe to captain Detroit was definitely Gordie. The legendary right-winger skippered the team between 1958 and 1962. The 21-time All-Star played 25 seasons with the club and won four Stanley Cups. He also led the league five times in goals scored and holds numerous franchise and league records and milestones. Howe played a league-record 1,767 regular-season games in his NHL career, scoring 801 goals and 1,850 points.

10. Another captain who skated his entire NHL career with Detroit was center Alex Delvecchio. He served as captain from 1962 to 1973 and as co-captain in 1973-74. He served just 383 minutes in penalties in 1,549 regular-season contests and scored 1,281 points. Delvecchio won three Stanley Cups as well as three Lady Byng Trophies for his sportsmanship. The Hall-of-Famer also served as Detroit's head coach and general manager later in life.

CHAPTER 6:

STATISTICALLY SPEAKING

QUIZ TIME!

1. This player led the Red Wings in scoring in 2019-20 with 53 points.

    a. Dylan Larkin
    b. Tyler Bertuzzi
    c. Anthony Mantha
    d. Robby Fabbri

2. This player leads the Red Wings in all-time plus-minus at +450.

    a. Chris Chelios
    b. Steve Yzerman
    c. Gordie Howe
    d. Nicklas Lidström

3. Which player leads the Red Wings in all-time goals per game at 0.56?

    a. John Ogrodnick
    b. Mickey Redmond

c. Dennis Hull

d. Brett Hull

4. Nicklas Lidström was on the ice for an even 3,000 regular-season goals during his career.

   a. True

   b. False

5. How many assists per game did Paul Coffey record as a Red Wing?

   a. 0.50

   b. 0.66

   c. 0.84

   d. 1.00

6. Which Hall-of-Famer finished his Red Wings career with 309 goals?

   a. Dino Ciccarelli

   b. Ted Lindsay

   c. Flash Hollett

   d. Brendan Shanahan

7. This goaltender played 95 games for the Red Wings.

   a. Gilles Gilbert

   b. Peter Ing

   c. Alan Bester

   d. Al Jensen

8. Who served a career team-record 218 minutes in penalties in the postseason?

a. Joey Kocur

b. Ted Lindsay

c. Bob Probert

d. Gordie Howe

9. This player recorded a team-record plus-17 rating in one playoff season.

a. Pierre Jarry

b. Jiri Hudler

c. Daniel Alfredsson

d. Daniel Cleary

10. The fastest 3 goals scored by the Red Wings in a regular-season game is?

a. 21 seconds

b. 28 seconds

c. 34 seconds

d. 42 seconds

11. The team record for shorthanded goals in a regular-season game is 5.

a. True

b. False

12. The highest number of power play goals scored in one regular-season game by Detroit is 6.

a. True

b. False

13. How long is the Red Wings' longest home undefeated streak?

a. 10 games

b. 12 games

c. 15 games

d. 23 games

14. Sergei Fedorov doesn't share the team record for 4 assists in one postseason period.

    a. True

    b. False

15. Who holds the team record for 6 points in one playoff game?

    a. Johan Franzen

    b. Dutch Reibel

    c. Carl Liscombe

    d. Vyacheslav Kozlov

16. What was the most goals allowed by Detroit in a playoff game?

    a. 8

    b. 9

    c. 11

    d. 13

17. How many points did defenseman Carl Brewer post in 70 regular-season games with Detroit?

    a. 0

    b. 10

    c. 39

    d. 48

18. Which goaltender posted 15 career shutouts as a Red Wing?

    a. Manny Legace
    b. John Ross Roach
    c. Roy Edwards
    d. Greg Stefan

19. This player served just 43 penalty minutes in 322 regular-season games with the franchise.

    a. Hal Hicks
    b. Joe Carveth
    c. Tom Webster
    d. John Chabot

20. Defender Bob Manno tallied 54 points in 136 regular-season outings with the Red Wings.

    a. True
    b. False

QUIZ ANSWERS

1. A – Dylan Larkin

2. D – Nicklas Lidström

3. B – Mickey Redmond

4. B - False

5. C – 0.84

6. D – Brendan Shanahan

7. A – Gilles Gilbert

8. D- Gordie Howe

9. D -Daniel Cleary

10. B – 28 seconds

11. B - False

12. A - True

13. D – 23

14. B -False

15. A – Johan Franzen

16. B - 9

17. C - 39

18. B – John Ross Roach

19. B – Joe Carveth

20. A -True

DID YOU KNOW?

1. The Red Wings have finished in last place in the NHL as well as first place and everywhere in between. Their finest regular season was 1995-96, when they went 62-13-7 for 131 points and a winning percentage of .799. Their worst season was 1985-86 with a mark of 17-57-6 for just 40 points and a .250 winning percentage.

2. Although Gordie Howe is the franchise leader in goals and points, the greatest individual campaign was enjoyed by Steve Yzerman in 1988-89. The young center set club records with 65 goals, 90 assists and 155 points. Yzerman is also the team's all-time assists leader with 1,063.

3. Steve Yzerman is also the franchise leader in playoff goals with 70 and points with 185, which he accumulated in 196 games. Defenseman Nicklas Lidström is right behind him at 183 points. Lidström scored 54 goals and a franchise-high 129 assists in the postseason; he did it in 263 games, which is also a club record.

4. Nicklas Lidström also holds several NHL records for a blue-liner. His 30 career playoff power play goals by a defenseman is the most ever. In addition, his 590 power play points in the regular season and 111 power play points in the postseason are league records for a defenseman.

5. At the end of the 2019-20 season, the Detroit franchise had made the playoffs in 64 of its 93 NHL campaigns and its

overall playoff record stood at 325 wins and 296 losses. However, the last time the team won a playoff series was in 2012-13, when they were eliminated in the second round.

6. Hall-of-Famer Terry Sawchuk leads Detroit goaltenders in most categories for regular-season play. He holds the franchise records for games played (734), wins (351), losses (243), ties (132) and shutouts (85). Sawchuk played in Detroit from 1949-50 to 1954-55 and again from 1957-58 to 1963-64. He won three Stanley Cups and three Vezina Trophies and won the 1951 Calder Trophy as the NHL rookie of the year with Detroit.

7. The top postseason goaltender in Detroit history is Chris Osgood. He leads the franchise in games played (110), wins (67), losses (37) and shutouts (14), and had a goals-against average of 2.02. Osgood broke in with the Red Wings in 1993-94 and stayed with the team until 2001. He was reacquired in 2005 and retired after the 2010-11 season. Osgood won three Stanley Cups in Detroit and shared the William M. Jennings Trophy twice, with Mike Vernon in 1996 and with Dominik Hasek in 2008.

8. One of the most physical Red Wings ever was winger Bob Probert. He holds the franchise record for penalty minutes in a season with 398, which he set in 1987-88. He also led the NHL in penalty minutes that campaign, when he also enjoyed his best offensive performance with 29 goals and 62 points. Probert is the all-time Detroit leader in career

penalty minutes with 2,090 and ranks fifth all-time in the NHL at 3,300. He passed away in July 2010 at the age of 45.

9. Head coach Scotty Bowman coached the team to a league-record 62 regular-season wins in 1995-96. This team and coaching record was tied by the Tampa Bay Lightning and head coach Jon Cooper in 2018-19. Bowman also owns Detroit playoff records for games coached with 134 and games won with 86. He guided the team to three Stanley Cups.

10. The biggest victory in Red Wings' history was a 15-0 whitewashing of the New York Rangers on Jan. 23, 1944. Their most embarrassing defeat came at the hands of the Toronto Maple Leafs on Jan. 2, 1971, when they were hammered 13-0 by Toronto at Maple Leaf Gardens.

CHAPTER 7:

THE TRADE MARKET

QUIZ TIME!

1. To which team did the Red Wings trade Pavel Datsyuk in 2016?

   a. Colorado Avalanche

   b. Arizona Coyotes

   c. Montreal Canadiens

   d. Los Angeles Kings

2. Which player did Detroit NOT receive from the Chicago Blackhawks for Ted Lindsay and Glenn Hall?

   a. Forbes Kennedy

   b. Johnny Wilson

   c. Jack McIntyre

   d. Hank Bassen

3. Detroit traded Sergei Fedorov to the Anaheim Ducks in 2003 for a 2nd-round draft pick.

   a. True

   b. False

4. Who was Dan McGillis traded for in 1996?

   a. Kirk Maltby

   b. Joe Kocur

   c. Kris Draper

   d. Mikael Renberg

5. How many trades did Detroit make in 2012-13?

   a. 10

   b. 7

   c. 3

   d. 2

6. To which team did the Red Wings trade Tomas Tatar in 2018 for three future draft picks?

   a. Dallas Stars

   b. Nashville Predators

   c. Montreal Canadiens

   d. Las Vegas Golden Knights

7. Who did Detroit receive from the Hartford Whalers in exchange for Paul Coffey and Keith Primeau?

   a. Jeff O'Neill & Brian Glynn

   b. Brendan Shanahan & Brian Glynn

   c. Kevin Dineen

   d. Geoff Sanderson & Brendan Shanahan

8. Detroit traded Vyacheslav Kozlov and a 2002 1st-round draft pick to obtain Dominik Hasek.

   a. True

   b. False

9. What did Detroit give up to Toronto for future Hall-of-Famer Larry Murphy?

   a. A 1st-round draft pick for 1996
   b. Terry Carkner and a 2nd-round draft pick
   c. Future considerations
   d. Cash

10. How many points did Mickey Redmond have in his first full season with the Red Wings after being traded by the Montreal Canadiens?

   a. 75
   b. 66
   c. 71
   d. 50

11. The Red Wings traded four players, including Terry Sawchuk, to the Boston Bruins for a lackluster return in 1955.

   a. True
   b. False

12. Where did the Red Wings send Gustav Nyquist in return for 2nd- and 3rd-round draft picks?

   a. Philadelphia Flyers
   b. San Jose Sharks
   c. Columbus Blue Jackets
   d. Minnesota Wild

13. Of the five players Detroit received from Boston for Terry Sawchuk, how many did they trade away that same year?

a. 2

b. 1

c. 4

d. 3

14. Garry Unger was traded to the St. Louis Blues because he did not cut his hair as per the general manager's rules.

a. True

b. False

15. In 1994, the Red Wings traded Steve Chiasson to the Calgary Flames and received who or what in return?

a. Joel Otto and a 2nd-round draft pick

b. Al MacInnis

c. Mike Vernon

d. Cash

16. Which player did Detroit get from the Nashville Predators in return for Patrick Eaves, Calle Jarnkrok, and a 2nd-round draft pick?

a. Kevin Klein

b. Taylor Beck

c. David Legwand

d. Joe Piskula

17. How many trades did Detroit make in the 2019-20 season?

a. 8

b. 10

c. 7

d. 13

18. Which player did the Red Wings get from Toronto in the Red Kelly trade in 1960?

    a. Marc Reaume
    b. Frank Mahovlich
    c. Bert Olmstead
    d. George Armstrong

19. Detroit sent a 3rd-round draft pick and cash to Ottawa for Daniel Alfredsson.

    a. True
    b. False

20. In 2012, Detroit was a part of a three-team trade that saw them send a 1st-round draft pick to which team?

    a. San Jose Sharks
    b. Colorado Avalanche
    c. Pittsburgh Penguins
    d. Tampa Bay Lightning

QUIZ ANSWERS

1. B – Arizona Coyotes

2. C – Jack McIntyre

3. B – False

4. A – Kirk Maltby

5. D – 2

6. D – Las Vegas Golden Knights

7. B – Brendan Shanahan & Brian Glynn

8. A – True

9. C – Future considerations

10. C – 71

11. A – True

12. B – San Jose Sharks

13. D – 3

14. A – True

15. C – Mike Vernon

16. C – David Legwand

17. A – 8

18. A – Marc Reaume

19. B – False

20. D – Tampa Bay Lightning

DID YOU KNOW?

1. Detroit received a good return from the Las Vegas Golden Knights in February 2018, when they acquired first-, second- and third-round draft picks for Tomas Tatar. The left-winger tallied 115 goals and 222 points with the Red Wings in 407 games and added 7 points in 17 playoff outings. Vegas traded Tatar to Montreal just seven months later.

2. Detroit picked up Brendan Shanahan and Brian Glynn in 1996 from the Hartford Whalers for Keith Primeau, Paul Coffey, and a first-round draft pick. Detroit appeared to give up a lot but Coffey's career was sliding and Primeau was asking for more money. Glynn never played a game with Detroit, but Shanahan helped the Red Wings win three Stanley Cups. He played nine seasons with the team and scored at least 25 goals each year, including three seasons with more than 40 goals.

3. One of the oddest transactions in modern-day NHL history saw the Red Wings acquire forward Kris Draper from the Winnipeg Jets in 1993 for $1! Draper went on to play 1,137 regular-season games in 17 seasons with Detroit and helped the squad win four Stanley Cups. He posted 158 goals and 361 points and won the 2004 Frank Selke Trophy as the league's best defensive forward.

4. One of the worst trades in Detroit history saw Marcel

Dionne and Bart Crashley head to Los Angeles for Dan Maloney, Terry Harper and a second-round draft pick. Dionne was drafted second overall by Detroit in 1971 and is now in the Hall of Fame. He had already notched 366 points in 309 games with Detroit and he finished his career with 1,771 points in 1,348 regular-season games. Maloney and Harper combined for 207 points with Detroit.

5. One of Detroit's best deals was landing defender Larry Murphy from the Toronto Maple Leafs for future considerations in March 1997. The Hall-of-Famer scored 171 points in 312 games with Detroit and was a plus-56. He added 34 points in 67 playoff games and helped the team win a pair of Stanley Cups.

6. The Red Wings bit the bullet when they sent 22-year-old goaltender Turk Broda to Toronto for $8,000 in 1936. Broda ended up in the Hall of Fame. The three-time All-Star won five Stanley Cups and two Vezina Trophies with Toronto in 14 seasons. He also led the NHL twice each in wins, goals-against average and shutouts.

7. Ken Holland made 54 trades as Detroit's general manager from 1997 to 2016 but one of the best moves he made was deciding not to trade a player. In 2007 the Red Wings were having a tough time signing unrestricted free agent Pavel Datsyuk to a new deal. Holland was about to trade his rights to New Jersey for Scott Gomez but then decided against it. Datsyuk re-signed with Detroit and tallied 390 points over the next five seasons while Gomez scored 236.

8. In 1955, the Red Wings had won four Stanley Cups in the past six seasons, but general manager Jack Adams traded Terry Sawchuk, who was the NHL's best goaltender, to Boston. The multi-player trade saw goaltender Gilles Boisvert arrive with Real Chevrefils, Ed Sanford, Norm Corcoran and Warren Godfrey. Detroit also shipped out Marc Bonin, Lorne Davis and Vic Stasiuk in the deal. The only player to remain in Detroit to help the team was Godfrey, who scored 100 points in 12 seasons.

9. The Red Wings reacquired Hall-of-Famer Sawchuk from Boston two years later when they traded forward Johnny Bucyk and cash for him. This proved to be costly, though, as Bucyk also ended up in the Hall of Fame. He played 23 NHL seasons with 556 goals and 1,369 points with almost all of that coming with Boston while winning two Stanley Cups and Lady Byng trophies. He was also a two-time All-Star.

10. In February 1960, Detroit tried to trade future Hall-of-Famer Red Kelly to the New York Rangers. However, Kelly said he would retire than report to the Rangers. The trade was nullified by the NHL and Kelly was then traded to Toronto for Marc Reaume. In seven seasons with the Maple Leafs, Kelly won four Stanley Cups to add to the four he had already won with Detroit. Reaume would play in just 47 games for the Red Wings.

CHAPTER 8:

DRAFT DAY

QUIZ TIME!

1. Which team originally drafted Dominik Hasek 199th overall in 1983?

    a. Buffalo Sabres

    b. Chicago Blackhawks

    c. Ottawa Senators

    d. St. Louis Blues

2. Who was drafted 95th overall in 2002?

    a. Valtteri Filppula

    b. Jiri Hudler

    c. Niklas Kronwall

    d. Jonathan Ericsson

3. The Detroit Red Wings had 10 draft picks in 1981.

    a. True

    b. False

4. Which year did the Red Wings select Steve Yzerman 4th overall?

   a. 1981

   b. 1982

   c. 1983

   d. 1984

5. Who was the first player ever drafted by the Red Wings?

   a. Steve Atkinson

   b. Rene Leclerc

   c. Bill Cosburn

   d. Pete Mahovlich

6. Who scored 33 points in his rookie season after being drafted 5th overall in 1975?

   a. Rick Lapointe

   b. Reed Larson

   c. Al Cameron

   d. Jerry Collins

7. What year was goaltender Jimmy Howard drafted?

   a. 2006

   b. 2002

   c. 2004

   d. 2003

8. The Red Wings have drafted only 13 players in the 7th round.

   a. True

   b. False

9. Mike Foligno was drafted 3rd overall by Detroit and scored how many goals in his career?

    a. 360
    b. 355
    c. 294
    d. 346

10. In what round was Steve Chiasson selected in the 1985 draft?

    a. 6th
    b. 2nd
    c. 4th
    d. 3rd

11. As of 2019, the Red Wings have only had three first overall draft picks.

    a. True
    b. False

12. How many total players had the Red Wings selected before the 2020 draft?

    a. 407
    b. 467
    c. 505
    d. 534

13. How many defensemen did the Red Wings select in the 1975 draft?

    a. 6
    b. 9

c. 5

d. 8

14. Of Detroit's 12 draft picks in 1986, only two never played an NHL game

    a. True

    b. False

15. How many goaltenders have the Red Wings drafted before 2020?

    a. 50

    b. 47

    c. 54

    d. 39

16. Who scored 72 points in his first season after being selected in the 1st round?

    a. Mike Foligno

    b. Willie Huber

    c. Dale McCourt

    d. Brent Peterson

17. Who did the Red Wings select 110th overall in 2012?

    a. Ryan Sproul

    b. Tyler Bertuzzi

    c. Martin Frk

    d. Andreas Athanasiou

18. Detroit selected which player 15th overall in the 2014 draft?

a. Mattias Janmark

b. Dylan Larkin

c. Evgeny Svechnikov

d. Christoffer Ehn

19. Through the 2019 draft, Jim Rutherford is the goalie drafted highest by Detroit.

a. True

b. False

20. Henrik Zetterberg was chosen in which round of the 1999 draft?

a. 7th

b. 3rd

c. 6th

d. 4th

QUIZ ANSWERS

1. B – Chicago Blackhawks

2. A – Valtteri Filppula

3. B – False

4. C – 1983

5. D – Pete Mahovlich

6. A – Rick Lapointe

7. D – 2003

8. B – False

9. B – 355

10. D – 3rd

11. A – True

12. C – 505

13. D – 8

14. A – True

15. B – 47

16. C – Dale McCourt

17. D – Andreas Athanasiou

18. B – Dylan Larkin

19. A – True

20. A – 7th

DID YOU KNOW?

1. The Detroit franchise has been around for almost a century and has suffered several woeful seasons, but they've had the first overall draft pick only three times as of 2019. The Red Wings have also had just 11 picks in the top five since the first amateur draft in 1963. In addition, the club didn't have a first-round pick in 12 seasons because they had traded it away.

2. The first time the Red Wings drafted first overall, they selected winger Claude Gauthier in 1964. In hindsight, this was a mistake because Hall of Fame goaltender Ken Dryden was selected in the third round. Gauthier was taken from Rosemont of the Quebec Major Junior Hockey League and never played an NHL game.

3. Detroit took center Dale McCourt first overall in 1977, and he led the team in scoring in three of his first four seasons. In 1978, the NHL ruled McCourt should be sent to the Los Angeles Kings as compensation for Detroit signing restricted free agent goalie Rogatien Vachon. McCourt refused to report and sued the league, the player's association, the Red Wings and the Kings. Detroit retained his rights after sending Andre St. Laurent and two first-round draft choices to LA.

4. The last time the Red Wings chose first overall was 1986, when they took forward Joe Murphy. He played just 90

games with the team before being traded to Edmonton as part of a blockbuster deal in 1989. Murphy scored 528 points in 779 NHL regular-season games, but Vincent Damphousse, who scored 1,205 points in 1,378 contests, went sixth in the same draft.

5. The best player the Red Wings drafted would be a toss-up between Hall of Fame centers Marcel Dionne and Steve Yzerman. Dionne was drafted second overall in 1971 and Yzerman went fourth in 1983. Dionne was traded to Los Angeles in 1975 and finished his career with 1,771 points in 1,348 regular-season games while Yzerman notched 1,755 points in 1,514 contests.

6. The Red Wings have drafted a total of 505 players up to 2020. They wasted several first-round draft picks between 1963 and 2015; six of them never played a game in the NHL and another six played fewer than 65 career games in the league.

7. The highest-drafted goaltender in franchise history was Jim Rutherford with the 10th overall pick in 1969. Rutherford played the 1970-71 season with Detroit and was then lost to Pittsburgh in the NHL Intra-League Draft. The Penguins traded him back to Detroit in 1974. The Red Wings then traded Rutherford to Toronto in 1980 and reacquired him as a free agent in 1982.

8. Some of Detroit's lowest draft picks have turned out to be hidden gems. Tomas Holmström was selected in the 10th round with the 257th overall pick in 1994. The winger

played 1,026 regular-season NHL games, compiling 243 goals and 530 points. He played his entire 15-year career with Detroit, added 97 points in 180 playoff games and won four Stanley Cups.

9. Another low-round draft pick was Henrik Zetterberg, who was taken with the 210th selection in 1999. The forward scored 337 goals and 960 points in 1,082 games with a plus-160 rating and added 57 goals and 120 points in 137 postseason outings. Zetterberg served as team captain for part of his 15-year career in Detroit. He won a Stanley Cup, a Conn Smythe Trophy and a King Clancy Memorial Trophy, and was named to an NHL Second All-Star Team.

10. Big center Pete Mahovlich was drafted second overall by Detroit in 1963 and the team traded for his famous brother Frank Mahovlich in a blockbuster deal in March 1968. They played together briefly as Pete was traded to Montreal in June 1969 and Hall-of-Famer Frank was dealt to Montreal in January 1971. Pete registered 90 points in 186 regular-season games with the Red Wings and Frank posted 196 in 198 appearances.

CHAPTER 9:

GOALTENDER TIDBITS

QUIZ TIME!

1. How many goals did Terry Richardson allow in 19 games between 1974 and 1977?

    a. 25

    b. 10

    c. 89

    d. 76

2. Terry Sawchuk accumulated a total of how many wins with the Red Wings?

    a. 346

    b. 352

    c. 361

    d. 338

3. On June 25, 2002, Dominik Hasek announced that he would retire.

    a. True

    b. False

4. The Red Wings used how many goalies in the 1974-75 season?

   a. 3
   b. 4
   c. 2
   d. 5

5. Which goaltender had 40 wins in the 1964-65 season?

   a. Carl Wetzel
   b. Hank Bassen
   c. Roger Crozier
   d. George Gardner

6. In 1956-57, what was Glenn Hall's save percentage with the Red Wings?

   a. .912
   b. .898
   c. .930
   d. .928

7. Who recorded 26 shutouts from 1944 to 1950?

   a. Normie Smith
   b. Harry Lumley
   c. Tom McGrattan
   d. Johnny Mowers

8. Before joining the Red Wings, John Ross Roach was the first goaltender to become a captain in 1924-25.

   a. True
   b. False

9. Which goaltender had 199 penalty minutes for Detroit?

   a. Eddie Mio

   b. Terry Sawchuk

   c. Gregg Stefan

   d. Chris Osgood

10. How many playoff wins did Chris Osgood have in Detroit?

    a. 67

    b. 70

    c. 55

    d. 60

11. Curtis Joseph played three full seasons in Detroit.

    a. True

    b. False

12. Who had a record of 7-34-6 in 1977?

    a. Ron Low

    b. Terry Richardson

    c. Ed Giacomin

    d. Jim Rutherford

13. Which goaltender won both of the two games he played in the 1991-92 season?

    a. Allan Bester

    b. Vincent Riendeau

    c. Scott King

    d. Alan Chevrier

14. Bob Sauve and Gilles Gilbert allowed 270 goals combined in 1981-82.

    a. True
    b. False

15. What was Chris Osgood's save percentage in the 2007-08 playoffs?

    a. .922
    b. .918
    c. .930
    d. .931

16. The Red Wings used a total of how many goalies in the 1973-74 season?

    a. 6
    b. 4
    c. 5
    d. 2

17. Other than Normie Smith, who won three games in the 1936-37 playoffs?

    a. Tiny Thompson
    b. Wilf Cude
    c. Jimmy Franks
    d. Earl Robertson

18. Tim Cheveldae assisted on how many Detroit goals?

    a. 13
    b. 19
    c. 15
    d. 12

19. Manny Legace won 112 of the 180 games he played for the Red Wings.

    a. True
    b. False

20. This goaltender had a .921 save percentage and 27 wins in 2015-16?

    a. Petr Mrazek
    b. Jimmy Howard
    c. Jonas Gustavsson
    d. Jared Coreau

QUIZ ANSWERS

1. D – 76

2. B – 350

3. A – True

4. B – 4

5. C – Roger Crozier

6. D – .928

7. B – Harry Lumley

8. A – True

9. C – Greg Stefan

10. A – 67

11. B – False

12. D – Jim Rutherford

13. B – Vincent Riendeau

14. A – True

15. C – .930

16. A – 6

17. D – Earl Robertson

18. C – 15

19. A – True

20. A – Petr Mrazek

DID YOU KNOW?

1. The most goalies used in one season by the Red Wings was six, which happened on two occasions. The first was in 1973-74, when Jim Rutherford, Doug Grant, Bill McKenzie, Terry Richardson, Roy Edwards and Denis DeJordy all saw action. In 1990-91, the team used Tim Cheveldae, Greg Hanlon, Alan Bester, Alain Chevrier, Scott King and Dave Gagnon.

2. Normie Smith holds the NHL record for the most saves in a game with 92. He accomplished that in the longest game in league history, when Smith beat the Montreal Maroons 1-0 in the 1935-36 Stanley Cup Final. The contest lasted 176 minutes and 30 seconds, ending in the sixth period of overtime. Smith won the Stanley Cup with the team in 1936 and 1937 as well as the Vezina Trophy and a First-Team All-Star selection in 1937.

3. Detroit had used 94 different netminders by the end of 2019-20. The only traditional league records any of them holds are the most ties in a career, the longest shutout streak and most consecutive games. Terry Sawchuk had 171 tie games in his career, with 130 of those as a Red Wing. Alec Connell holds the shutout streak at 460 minutes and 49 seconds, but he set it before arriving in Detroit. In addition, when Glenn Hall played 502 straight games from 1955 to 1962, the streak started in Detroit and ended when he was with Chicago.

4. Glenn Hall cracked the Red Wing starting lineup in 1955-56 when he won the Calder Trophy as NHL rookie of the year and was named a Second-Team All-Star after posting 12 shutouts and playing every game. Hall played every game again in his second season and made the First All-Star Team. He was then traded to Chicago in July 1957 and his streak continued until November 1962.

5. Goaltender Dominik Hasek was acquired in a trade with Buffalo in July 2001. He won two Stanley Cups with Detroit and shares the club records for playoff games in a season with Chris Osgood at 23 and wins in a playoff season with Osgood and Mike Vernon at 16. In addition, Hasek holds the club record for 6 shutouts in a playoff campaign as well as minutes played in a playoffs season at 1,455.

6. The only Red Wings netminder to score a goal was Chris Osgood. He did it against the Hartford Whalers on March 6, 1996. Osgood won three Stanley Cups with Detroit and shared the William M. Jennings Trophy with Mike Vernon in 1995-96. He also led the league in goals-against average (2.17) and wins (39) that season and was named a Second-Team All-Star.

7. Chris Osgood also shares the franchise record for career assists by a goalie with 15, along with Tim Cheveldae and Greg Stefan. Cheveldae holds the club record for assists in one season (1990-91) while Osgood holds the mark for 4 career playoff assists and shares the record with Cheveldae

and Stefan for 2 assists in one playoff season. Because of his goal, Osgood leads Detroit goalies in career points with 16.

8. Curtis Joseph holds the best save percentage by a Detroit goalie in the playoffs since the NHL started recording the statistic. Joseph's career save percentage with the team in the postseason was .931. He was signed as a free agent in July 2002 and left for Phoenix as a free agent three years later. Even though Joseph sparkled in the postseason and had a goals-against average of just 1.64, his postseason record with Detroit was only 4-8 in 13 games.

9. Hall of Fame goalie Eddie Giacomin starred with the New York Rangers, but many fans may not know he finished his career with the Red Wings. He was a five-time All-Star and Vezina Trophy winner with the Rangers before Detroit claimed the 36-year-old on waivers in 1975. Giacomin played 71 regular-season games over three seasons with the Red Wings, recording an .883 save percentage and a 3.47 goals-against average.

10. The name Wilf Cude won't resonate with most fans because the British-born goalie played for Detroit back in 1933-34. Cude was actually loaned to the team by Montreal for half the season in return for cash. He stood on his head by going 15-6-8 with a 1.52 goals-against average and four shutouts in 29 games. He then went 4-5 in the playoffs with a 2.13 goals-against average.

CHAPTER 10:

ODDS & ENDS

QUIZ TIME!

1. What was the Red Wings' faceoff win percentage in 2018-19?

    a. 54.0

    b. 50.8

    c. 49.7

    d. 51.4

2. Henrik Zetterberg blocked 267 shots during his career with the Red Wing.

    a. True

    b. False

3. How many goals did the Red Wings score in a victory against the New York Rangers on January 1, 1944?

    a. 20

    b. 13

    c. 16

    d. 15

4. Detroit scored a total of how many goals in the 1951-52 playoffs?

   a. 9
   b. 13
   c. 24
   d. 25

5. Through the end of the 2019-20 regular season, how many overall points has Detroit recorded?

   a. 6,951
   b. 6,499
   c. 6,928
   d. 5,963

6. How many Stanley Cups did Scotty Bowman win as the Red Wings coach?

   a. 2
   b. 1
   c. 4
   d. 3

7. How many years was Jack Adams involved with the Red Wings as coach and general manager?

   a. 29
   b. 36
   c. 40
   d. 31

8. Thomas Vanek scored on all 5 of his shootout attempts in 2016-17.

a. True

b. False

9. How many total goals combined did the Red Wings score in the Detroit Olympia and Joe Louis Arena?

    a. 10,598

    b. 10,600

    c. 9,835

    d. 9,958

10. How many players have appeared in at least one game for the franchise since its NHL debut?

    a. 926

    b. 878

    c. 950

    d. 947

11. Who scored the game-winning goal in 1996-97 to give the Red Wings their eighth Stanley Cup?

    a. Larry Murphy

    b. Doug Brown

    c. Darren McCarty

    d. Nicklas Lidström

12. Mike Babcock led the Red Wings to a total of 1,050 points as coach from 2006 to 2015.

    a. True

    b. False

13. How many head coaches has Detroit had?

a. 25

b. 22

c. 27

d. 30

14. The Red Wings recorded at least 100 points for 12 straight seasons.

    a. True

    b. False

15. Against which team did Gordie Howe score his first NHL goal?

    a. Chicago Blackhawks

    b. Montreal Canadiens

    c. New York Rangers

    d. Toronto Maple Leafs

16. Who did the Red Wings beat to win their first playoff series?

    a. Toronto Maple Leafs

    b. Montreal Maroons

    c. Ottawa Senators

    d. New York Americans

17. Which player scored the first-ever hat trick for Detroit in 1927?

    a. Duke Keats

    b. Johnny Shepard

    c. Pete Bellefeuille

    d. Fred Gordon

18. How many playoff games did it take the Red Wings to win their first Stanley Cup?

   a. 6
   b. 8
   c. 7
   d. 9

19. Detroit did not lose a game in the 1951-52 playoffs.

   a. True
   b. False

20. The Red Wings have won how many division championships.

   a. 20
   b. 19
   c. 14
   d. 16

QUIZ ANSWERS

1. B – 50.8

2. A – True

3. D – 15

4. C – 24

5. C – 6,928

6. D – 3

7. B – 36

8. A – True

9. A – 10,598

10. D – 947

11. C – Darren McCarty

12. B – False

13. C – 27

14. A – True

15. D – Toronto Maple Leafs

16. B – Montreal Maroons

17. A – Duke Keats

18. C – 7

19. A – True

20. B – 19

DID YOU KNOW?

1. One of the strangest hockey traditions in Detroit involves fans throwing an octopus onto the ice for good luck in the playoffs. This oddity first reared its head in 1952, when the owner of a local seafood market tossed the creature from the stands. Since it took eight wins to capture the Stanley Cup back then, each of the octopus' eight legs represented one victory. The good luck charm worked, as Detroit went 8-0 to capture the championship that season.

2. Former Red Wings' owner James E. Norris Sr. was also a co-owner of both the New York Rangers and Chicago Black Hawks. Norris and his son, James D. Norris, were inducted into the Hockey Hall of Fame, along with another son and former Red Wings' owner Bruce Norris. However, his daughter Marguerite, who co-owned the franchise with Bruce and was team president between 1952 and 1955, wasn't inducted.

3. The franchise has had 27 head coaches since joining the NHL. Jack Adams holds the record for most games coached with 964. However, Mike Babcock holds the team's career records for wins with 458 and Scotty Bowman holds the postseason record with 86 wins. Eight former Detroit coaches were inducted into the Hall of Fame as players and two as builders. Bobby Kromm, Jacques Demers and Bowman all won the Jack Adams Award as coach of the season with the Wings.

4. Twelve different men have held the position of Detroit general manager over the years. Art Duncan was the franchise's first in 1926. He was followed in succession by Jack Adams, Sid Abel, Ned Harkness, Alex Delvecchio, Ted Lindsay, Jimmy Skinner, Jim Devellano, Bryan Murray, Jim Devellano (again), Ken Holland and Steve Yzerman.

5. While Art Duncan served as Detroit's general manager in the club's inaugural season, he was also the team's captain, head coach and one of its defensemen. Jack Adams then took over as general manager and coach in 1927-28. He remained behind the bench until 1946-47 and as general manager until 1962-63.

6. In 1938, Detroit and the Montreal Canadiens became the first NHL franchises to play in Europe when they staged exhibition contests in London and Paris. The teams played nine times with Detroit winning three, losing five and tying one.

7. The Red Wings reached the Stanley Cup Final for the first time in 1933-34 but were beaten in four games of the best-of-five series by the Chicago Black Hawks. Detroit won its first Stanley Cup two seasons later by downing the Toronto Maple Leafs in four games and then made it two in a row by edging the New York Rangers in five outings the following season.

8. In 1957, Ted Lindsay helped create the National Hockey League Players' Association (NHLPA) with Montreal

Canadien defenseman and fellow Hall-of-Famer Doug Harvey. This didn't sit well with owner Bruce Norris and Lindsay was promptly swapped to Chicago with goaltender Glenn Hall.

9. Red Wings center Norm Ullman set a playoff record for the fastest two goals on April 11, 1965, when he scored twice in five seconds against the Chicago Blackhawks. Ullman was with Detroit from 1955-56 to 1968. He was then involved in a blockbuster trade when he was dealt to Toronto with Floyd Smith and Paul Henderson for Frank Mahovlich, Garry Unger, Pete Stemkowski, and the rights to Carl Brewer. Ullman and Mahovlich are enshrined in the Hockey Hall of Fame.

10. Fox Sports Detroit holds the television rights to Red Wings games and features commentary from former players Mickey Redmond, Chris Osgood and Larry Murphy. Former player Paul Woods is a radio analyst on Red Wings' games and four members of the organization have won the Foster Hewitt Memorial Award: Budd Lynch, Bruce Martyn, Dave Strader and Redmond. The first local TV broadcast of a Red Wings contest took place in 1949.

CHAPTER 11:

RED WINGS ON THE BLUE LINE

QUIZ TIME!

1. How many points did Red Kelly post with the Red Wings?

   a. 402

   b. 378

   c. 472

   d. 437

2. Who was the only defenseman who had 10 points in Detroit's inaugural season?

   a. Art Duncan

   b. Harold Halderson

   c. Hobie Kitchen

   d. Clem Loughlin

3. Mike Green recorded 47 points in 66 games in the 2017-18 season.

   a. True

   b. False

4. Nicklas Lidström totaled how many assists in 2005-06?

    a. 57
    b. 64
    c. 44
    d. 61

5. Which defenseman had 37 points and 88 penalty minutes in 1961-62?

    a. Bill Gadsby
    b. Warren Godfrey
    c. Gerry Odrowski
    d. Pete Goegan

6. Who had a plus-minus of +16 in the 1996-97 playoffs?

    a. Aaron Ward
    b. Nicklas Lidström
    c. Viacheslav Fetisov
    d. Larry Murphy

7. Börje Salming recorded how many assists in 1989-90?

    a. 23
    b. 14
    c. 17
    d. 8

8. A total of 12 defensemen played for Detroit in the 1976-77 season.

    a. True
    b. False

9. In 2003-04, how many defensemen scored at least 15 points?

   a. 5
   b. 3
   c. 6
   d. 2

10. Which defenseman had a total of 163 penalty minutes in the 1965-66 regular season and playoffs combined?

    a. Bob McCord
    b. Bert Marshall
    c. Bryan Watson
    d. Jim Watson

11. Paul Coffey scored 14 goals in each of his four seasons with the Red Wings.

    a. True
    b. False

12. Against which team did Red Kelly score his first hat trick in 1954?

    a. Chicago Blackhawks
    b. Montreal Canadiens
    c. New York Rangers
    d. Boston Bruins

13. Who had 31 points and a plus-11 rating in 2014-15?

    a. Jakub Kindl
    b. Niklas Kronwall
    c. Danny DeKeyser
    d. Jonathan Ericsson

14. Niklas Kronwall scored 4 game-winning goals in 2011-12.

    a. True
    b. False

15. How many blocked shots did Brian Rafalski have in 2009-10?

    a. 79
    b. 101
    c. 113
    d. 94

16. Chris Chelios had a total of how many minutes of ice time in Detroit?

    a. 12,800
    b. 12,171
    c. 11,539
    d. 10,967

17. How many hits did Jonathan Ericsson dole out in 2018-19?

    a. 83
    b. 76
    c. 98
    d. 100

18. How many games did Lee Norwood play to tally 31 points in 1987-88?

    a. 51
    b. 60
    c. 49
    d. 57

19. Detroit blue-liners combined for 44 assists in the 2007-08 playoffs.

    a. True
    b. False

20. How many assists per game did Paul Coffey average in 1994-95?

    a. 1.07
    b. 0.99
    c. 1.13
    d. 0.98

QUIZ ANSWERS

1. C – 472

2. D – Clem Loughlin

3. B – False

4. B – 64

5. A – Bill Gadsby

6. D – Larry Murphy

7. C – 17

8. A – True

9. A – 5

10. C – Bryan Watson

11. B – False

12. D – Boston Bruins

13. C – Danny DeKeyser

14. A – True

15. B – 101

16. B – 12,171

17. C – 98

18. A – 51

19. A – True

20. D – 0.98

DID YOU KNOW?

1. There are 19 former Detroit blue-liners in the Hockey Hall of Fame. They are Al Arbour, Nicklas Lidström, Paul Coffey, Larry Murphy, Chris Chelios, Viacheslav Fetisov, Doug Harvey, Mark Howe, Red Kelly, Leo Boivin, Bill Gadsby, Ebbie Goodfellow, Reg Noble, Brad Park, Marcel Pronovost, Bill Quackenbush, Earl Siebert, Jack Stewart and Börje Salming. Noble, Kelly and Goodfellow also played forward during their careers.

2. Gordie Howe's son, Mark Howe, patrolled the blue line for Detroit from 1992-93 through 1994-95, which were the last three seasons of his career. Mark and his brother Marty played with their father Gordie in the World Hockey Association (WHA). After playing with the Hartford Whalers and Philadelphia Flyers, Mark signed with Detroit as a free agent, chipping in with 64 points in 122 regular-season contests.

3. One of the NHL's toughest defensemen was Jim Schoenfeld, who was traded to Detroit in 1981. The former Buffalo captain's body couldn't handle the wear and tear much more, though, and he played just 96 regular-season games with the club, posting 25 points. He then signed as a free agent with Boston and retired two years later at the age of 32.

4. One of the most underrated defensemen in NHL history

was Ron Stackhouse, who posted 459 points in 859 career regular-season games. He was acquired in a 1971 trade with the California Golden Seals and tallied 80 points in 184 regular-season games with Detroit. He was then traded to Pittsburgh in 1974.

5. Terry Harper was a rugged, stay-at-home defender who helped Montreal win five Stanley Cups and then served as captain of Los Angeles for two years. Harper was a part of the infamous trade that saw Marcel Dionne move west to LA in 1975. Harper totaled 70 points in 252 regular-season games with the Red Wings before joining St. Louis as a 40-year-old free agent.

6. Blue-liner Reed Larson was drafted 22nd overall by Detroit in 1976 and stayed until 1985-86. He captained the squad in 1981-82 and was co-captain the season before. He notched 19 goals and 60 points as a rookie to finish fifth in Calder Trophy voting. Larson scored more than 20 goals in five of his seasons in Detroit and totaled 188 goals and 570 points in 708 regular-season encounters.

7. Flash Hollett was a two-time Stanley Cup winner when he landed in Detroit in 1944 from Boston. He had excellent puck handling and skating skills and played his last three seasons with the Red Wings. The former lacrosse player scored 20 goals in his second campaign in 50 games. Hollett posted 72 points in 115 regular-season contests and, when he retired in 1946, his 313 points made him the NHL's highest-scoring defenseman at the time.

8. Chris Chelios had a big impact on the Red Wings after being acquired in a trade with Chicago in 1999. He helped the club win two Stanley Cups and chipped in with 152 points and a plus-158 rating in 578 regular-season games. Chelios was inducted into the Hall of Fame following his career, which included three Stanley Cups and Norris trophies, a Mark Messier Leadership Award, and seven All-Star berths.

9. Reg Noble was one of the few players who skated with all three versions of the Detroit franchise: the Falcons, Cougars and Red Wings. The former captain played defense but could also play center when needed. He joined Detroit in 1927 via a trade with the Montreal Maroons for $7,500 and spent six seasons with the team before being dealt back to the Maroons.

10. Gary Bergman was an underrated player who took care of his own end first. He ranks second behind Reed Larson in all-time franchise penalty minutes for a defenseman with 1,103 in 706 regular-season contests. He also had enough offensive acumen to chip in with 60 goals and 303 points from 1964 to 1975.

CHAPTER 12:

CENTERS OF ATTENTION

QUIZ TIME!

1. How many goals did Steve Yzerman score in 1987-88?

    a. 43
    b. 58
    c. 65
    d. 50

2. Which center tallied 86 points in the 1980-81 season?

    a. Dale McCourt
    b. Paul Woods
    c. Brent Peterson
    d. Mark Kirton

3. Darren Helm won 403 faceoffs in 2011-12.

    a. True
    b. False

4. What was Pavel Datsyuk's plus-minus in 2007-08?

    a. + 14
    b. + 22

c. + 38

d. + 41

5. This player recorded 24 assists in 1944-45.

    a. Carl Liscombe

    b. Don Grosso

    c. Murray Armstrong

    d. Syd Howe

6. Which center scored 16 power play goals in 1962-63?

    a. Bruce MacGregor

    b. Alex Delvecchio

    c. Norm Ullman

    d. Parker MacDonald

7. In which season did Valtteri Filppula score 66 points?

    a. 2011-12

    b. 2012-13

    c. 2014-15

    d. 2010-11

8. A total of 14 centers played for Detroit in 2014-15.

    a. True

    b. False

9. How many goals did Igor Larionov contribute in the 2001-02 playoffs?

    a. 6

    b. 5

    c. 4

    d. 8

10. In a 10-3 victory over the St. Louis Blues in 1991, how many goals were scored by Detroit centers?

    a. 3
    b. 1
    c. 2
    d. 4

11. Dennis Polonich served 1,242 penalty minutes in only 390 games played.

    a. True
    b. False

12. In the 1954-55 playoffs, how many goals did Red Wing centers score?

    a. 20
    b. 14
    c. 5
    d. 0

13. Who scored 10 game-winning goals in 1964-65?

    a. Ted Hampson
    b. Pit Martin
    c. Eddie Joyal
    d. Norm Ullman

14. Steve Yzerman had 6 penalty shot attempts in his career.

    a. True
    b. False

15. How many assists did Pavel Datsyuk register in 2007-08?

a. 61

b. 54

c. 66

d. 69

16. Who tallied 68 points in 1969-70?

a. Garry Unger

b. Al Karlander

c. Billy Dea

d. Alex Delvecchio

17. In which season did Marcel Dionne tally 74 assists?

a. 1975-76

b. 1974-75

c. 1979-80

d. 1977-78

18. How many points did Dylan Larkin score in his rookie season?

a. 50

b. 32

c. 45

d. 39

19. Sergei Fedorov notched 79 game-winning goals as a Red Wing.

a. True

b. False

20. In 1988-89, how many Detroit centers scored more than 10 goals?

a. 4
b. 6
c. 3
d. 2

QUIZ ANSWERS

1. D – 50

2. A – Dale McCourt

3. A – True

4. D – + 41

5. C – Murray Armstrong

6. D – Parker MacDonald

7. A – 2011-12

8. B – False

9. B – 5

10. C – 2

11. A – True

12. B – 14

13. D – Norm Ullman

14. A – True

15. C – 66

16. D – Alex Delvecchio

17. B – 1974-75

18. C – 45

19. A – True

20. D – 2

DID YOU KNOW?

1. Former Detroit centers who are in the Hall of Fame are Sid Abel, Marty Barry, Alex Delvecchio, Marcel Dionne, Bernie Federko, Sergei Fedorov, Frank Foyston, Frank Fredrickson, Duke Keats, Igor Larionov, Mike Modano, Darryl Sittler, Steve Yzerman, Václav Nedomanský, Adam Oates, Norm Ullman and Carl Voss.

2. Carl Voss was bought by Detroit from the New York Rangers in 1932-33 and was named the first winner of the NHL's rookie of the year award. However, he was traded to the Ottawa Senators after just eight games the next season. Inducted into the Hockey Hall of Fame as a builder, he was also an excellent football player who won the Grey Cup with the Queen's University team in 1924.

3. Detroit's "Production Line" was centered by Sid Abel, who joined the club in 1938. He was named captain in 1942 but left the team the following year to join the Royal Canadian Air Force during the Second World War. He returned in 1946, and the four-time All-Star won the Hart Memorial Trophy and three Stanley Cups with Detroit. His number 12 was retired by the club. He coached the team from 1957 to 1970 with a one-season break in 1968-69, and served as general manager from April 1963 to January 1971.

4. The first hockey player to defect from Eastern Europe to North America was Václav Nedomanský, who was born

in the former nation of Czechoslovakia. After being named the top forward in the 1974 world championships, he defected to Canada and started his pro career in the World Hockey Association (WHA). Nedomanský was traded to Detroit in 1977 and posted 247 points in 364 regular-season games.

5. The feistiest center in franchise history was Dennis Polonich, even though he was just 5 feet and 6 inches tall. The one-time captain served 1,242 penalty minutes in 390 regular-season games and played his entire career with Detroit. Polonich, who occasionally played the wing, was awarded $850,000 in 1982 lawsuit after requiring reconstructive surgery to his face when Wilf Paiement of Colorado attacked him on the ice.

6. Pavel Datsyuk won two Stanley Cups with Detroit as well as three straight Frank Selke trophies as the NHL's best defensive forward and four consecutive Lady Byng trophies for sportsmanship. His NHL career spanned from 2001-02 through 2015-16 and was spent entirely in Detroit. He posted 918 points in 953 games and added 113 points in 157 playoff matches.

7. Walt McKechnie was an unheralded center with Detroit who was originally acquired in a 1975 trade with Boston. He stayed until August 1977, when he was dealt to Washington. McKechnie was then signed as a free agent by Detroit at the age of 34 in 1981 and spent his final two seasons with the team. He played 321 regular-season

games in two stints with the Red Wings, compiling 256 points, 11 power play goals and nine shorthanded markers.

8. Igor Larionov was drafted 214th overall by Vancouver in 1985, but wound up in the Hall of Fame. Detroit picked him up in a 1995 trade with San Jose, and he went on to win three Stanley Cups with the team. He tallied 397 points in 539 games with Detroit and had a plus-102 rating.

9. Long-haired Ron Duguay had a reputation as a being bit of a playboy when he was with the New York Rangers, but the Red Wings recognized his hockey talent and picked him up in a 1983 trade. Duguay didn't disappoint as he contributed 217 points in 227 regular-season games. However, Detroit traded the center-winger to Pittsburgh for Doug Shedden in March 1986.

10. The latest Red Wing to star at center ice is Dylan Larkin, who was drafted 15th overall in 2014. Larkin notched 23 goals and 45 points as a rookie, starting the season as a 19-year-old. He registered 32 goals and 73 points in 76 games in 2018-19. Through the end of the 2019-20 season, Larkin has 266 points in 389 regular-season outings.

CHAPTER 13:

THE WINGERS TAKE FLIGHT

QUIZ TIME!

1. How many points did Gordie Howe score in his rookie season?

    a. 22

    b. 38

    c. 9

    d. 19

2. Winger-center Henrik Zetterberg scored how many power play goals in his career?

    a. 95

    b. 77

    c. 100

    d. 89

3. Bob Probert served 398 penalty minutes in 1987-88.

    a. True

    b. False

4. How many hat tricks did Frank Mahovlich tally in 1968-69?

    a. 3
    b. 2
    c. 5
    d. 4

5. Which winger earned 23 assists in 1935-36?

    a. John Sorrell
    b. Syd Howe
    c. Larry Aurie
    d. Herbie Lewis

6. Mike Foligno scored how many goals with the Red Wings?

    a. 28
    b. 40
    c. 77
    d. 116

7. Which center played right wing in 1995-96 and scored 11 game-winning goals?

    a. Steve Yzerman
    b. Sergei Fedorov
    c. Adam Oates
    d. Kris Draper

8. Vyacheslav Kozlov scored 4 goals in an 11-1 victory over the Montreal Canadiens in 1995.

    a. True
    b. False

9. How many left-wingers played for Detroit in 1933-34?

    a. 5
    b. 8
    c. 7
    d. 6

10. Daniel Alfredsson scored how many points in his only season with Detroit?

    a. 13
    b. 33
    c. 49
    d. 40

11. Gordie Howe played 1,767 career games with the Red Wings.

    a. True
    b. False

12. How many wingers scored in an 8 - 2 win on March 26, 2000, against the New York Rangers?

    a. 2
    b. 0
    c. 4
    d. 3

13. Which left-winger scored 23 goals on 155 shots on net in 1977-78?

    a. Dan Maloney
    b. Nick Libett
    c. Paul Woods
    d. Dennis Hull

14. Tom Webster had a minus-48 rating in 1970-71.

    a. True
    b. False

15. How old was Brett Hull when he scored 76 points with the Red Wings in 2002-03?

    a. 37
    b. 40
    c. 39
    d. 38

16. How many faceoffs did Henrik Zetterberg win from the 2007-08 season through the 2017-18 season?

    a. 3,890
    b. 5,863
    c. 5,797
    d. 4,902

17. Who had 24 assists in 2017-18?

    a. Gustav Nyquist
    b. Justin Abdelkader
    c. Anthony Mantha
    d. Martin Frk

18. How many points did Ted Lindsay score for Detroit in 123 playoff appearances?

    a. 88
    b. 67
    c. 45
    d. 90

19. Todd Bertuzzi played in Detroit for 6 years; how many games did he play?

    a. 400
    b. 308
    c. 379
    d. 345

20. Left wing Parker MacDonald led the Red Wings with 83 points in 1964-65.

    a. True
    b. False

QUIZ ANSWERS

1. A – 22

2. C – 100

3. A – True

4. D – 4

5. D – Herbie Lewis

6. C – 77

7. B – Sergei Fedorov

8. A – True

9. C – 7

10. C – 49

11. B – False

12. D – 3

13. B – Nick Libett

14. A – True

15. D – 38

16. B – 5,863

17. C – Anthony Mantha

18. A – 88

19. B – 308

20. B – False

DID YOU KNOW?

1. Hall of Fame wingers who played for Detroit are Gordie Howe, Andy Bathgate, Johnny Bucyk, Dino Ciccarelli, Charlie Conacher, Roy Conacher, Syd Howe, Brett Hull, Herbie Lewis, Ted Lindsay, Frank Mahovlich, Bud Poile, Luc Robitaille, Brendan Shanahan, Jack Walker, Harry Watson, George Hay and Ralph "Cooney" Weiland.

2. In 1959, Andy Bathgate was the source for a magazine article titled "Atrocities on Ice." He was upset with the amount of spearing in the NHL and named Gordie Howe as the meanest player in the league. He was fined $100 for the article at a time when his annual salary was $18,000. Bathgate eventually became a teammate of Howe's, playing for Detroit from 1965 to 1967.

3. Dino Ciccarelli was another former Red Wing who was fined, but his was levied by a court of law rather than the NHL. While playing with the Minnesota North Stars in Toronto in 1988, the winger attacked defenseman Luke Richardson with his hockey stick. He was convicted of assault, fined $1,000 and sentenced to a day in jail. Ciccarelli's 608 career goals are the most by a player who was available in the draft but not selected.

4. Three Conacher brothers are in the Hall of Fame – Lionel, Roy and Charlie – and two of them skated with the Red Wings. Roy arrived in 1946 in a trade from Boston and led

the team in scoring in 1946-47. However, he wanted more money ($8,500) than general manager Jack Adams was willing to pay and was promptly traded to the New York Rangers in 1947. Conacher refused to report and the deal was nullified. Chicago was given permission to negotiate with Conacher, and he was then sold to the Blackhawks.

5. Charlie Conacher was bought from Toronto for $16,000 in and posted 22 points in 40 games in 1938-39 to finish fourth in team scoring. Although he was just 30 years old, the Red Wings let him leave after the season as injuries caught up with him. In 1950, when coaching the Chicago Blackhawks, Conacher reportedly struck a Detroit reporter after suffering a 9-2 loss to the Red Wings. He apologized but was fined $200 by the NHL.

6. Another winger from a famous family was Brett Hull, who played with Detroit for three seasons after signing as a 37-year-old free agent in 2001. Like his famous father, Bobby Hull, Brett was a pure goal scorer. He notched 92 goals and 207 points in 245 games with 13 goals and 24 points in 39 playoff contests. His 10 playoff goals in 2001-02 led the league and helped Detroit win the Stanley Cup.

7. When it comes to shooting accuracy and consistency, Ray Sheppard was second to none. The winger leads all Detroit players who appeared in over 80 games in career shooting percentage at 20.1 He tallied 265 points in 274 regular-season games between 1991 and October 1995, when he was traded to San Jose for Igor Larionov.

8. Mickey Redmond was acquired when Frank Mahovlich was traded to Montreal in 1971. The winger played 317 career games with Detroit before retiring in 1976 at the age of 28 due to a back injury. Redmond scored 177 goals and 309 points and earned two All-Star berths. He led the NHL in power play goals in 1973-74 with a team-record 21 and was the first Detroit player to score 50 goals in a season.

9. John Ogrodnick scored 265 goals and 546 points in 558 regular-season contests with Detroit. He was a power play specialist: he earned 171 points with the man advantage and he chipped in with 10 shorthanded goals. He also led the team in goals in six straight seasons. Ogrodnick peaked in 1984-85 with 55 goals and 105 points and was named a First-Team All-Star.

10. Bob Probert is the all-time penalty leader with Detroit, but Joey Kocur holds a couple of team records. Kocur holds the record for 42 penalty minutes in a game and 37 minutes in a period, both of which he set against St. Louis in 1985. He served 1,963 minutes with Detroit in 535 games and another 147 minutes in the postseason. Kocur led the league with 377 minutes in 1985-86, and his toughness helped Detroit win two Stanley Cups.

CHAPTER 14:

THE HEATED RIVALRIES

QUIZ TIME!

1. Which Original Six team have the Red Wings faced 739 times in the regular season?

    a. Chicago Blackhawks
    b. Montreal Canadiens
    c. Boston Bruins
    d. Toronto Maple Leafs

2. How many times did the Red Wings and the Colorado Avalanche meet in the playoffs between 1995 and 2002?

    a. 4
    b. 6
    c. 5
    d. 7

3. A total of 279 penalty minutes was handed out to Detroit and Toronto on January 13, 1986.

    a. True
    b. False

4. How many of the 13 meetings did Detroit lose to the Tampa Bay Lightning from 2016 until the end of the 2018-19 season?

    a. 13
    b. 11
    c. 9
    d. 12

5. How many goals have the Red Wings scored against the Boston Bruins in 607 meetings?

    a. 1,740
    b. 1,170
    c. 1,901
    d. 1,813

6. What was the final score of Detroit's win over the Chicago Blackhawks in the 2009 Winter Classic?

    a. 4-1
    b. 7-3
    c. 6-4
    d. 6-2

7. Detroit has recorded how many goals in 127 games against the Colorado Avalanche?

    a. 429
    b. 412
    c. 355
    d. 420

8. Goaltender Patrick Roy demanded to be traded from Montreal after Detroit scored 9 goals on him in a 1995 game.

   a. True
   b. False

9. Which team did the Red Wings lose to twice in Sweden in 2009-10?

   a. Minnesota Wild
   b. St. Louis Blues
   c. Philadelphia Flyers
   d. Chicago Blackhawks

10. How many games did Detroit lose at the old Montreal Forum?

   a. 188
   b. 190
   c. 186
   d. 203

11. Detroit lost its first NHL game to the New York Americans.

   a. True
   b. False

12. What was the final score in a double-digit victory over the Boston Bruins on Dec. 2, 1965?

   a. 10 -2
   b. 13 - 4
   c. 11 - 1
   d. 10 - 0

13. How many goals did the Red Wings score against the Chicago Blackhawks in the 2001-02 season?

    a. 12
    b. 9
    c. 20
    d. 16

14. In the 2008-09 playoffs, Detroit swept every team except the Colorado Avalanche.

    a. True
    b. False

15. What team did the Red Wings face in a nine-game series in the NHL's first-ever European tour?

    a. New York Rangers
    b. Dallas Stars
    c. Montreal Canadiens
    d. Quebec Nordiques

16. How many goals did the Red Wings score against the Nashville Predators in 1998-99?

    a. 23
    b. 24
    c. 18
    d. 20

17. Which team has scored 1,630 goals against Detroit in 93 seasons?

    a. Boston Bruins
    b. Philadelphia Flyers

c. New York Rangers

d. Toronto Maple Leafs

18. How many fights were recorded in Red Wings' games against the former Minnesota North Stars club?

a. 124

b. 134

c. 140

d. 105

19. How many goals did Detroit score against the Pittsburgh Penguins to win the Stanley Cup Final in 2008?

a. 11

b. 14

c. 20

d. 17

20. From 1950 to 1956, the Red Wings won all five playoff meetings with the Toronto Maple Leafs.

a. True

b. False

QUIZ ANSWERS

1. A – Chicago Black Hawks

2. C – 5

3. A – True

4. A – 13

5. D – 1,813

6. C – 6-4

7. D – 420

8. A – True

9. B – St. Louis Blues

10. C – 186

11. B – False

12. A – 10-2

13. D – 16

14. B – False

15. C – Montreal Canadiens

16. A – 23

17. C – New York Rangers

18. B – 134

19. D – 17

20. A – True

DID YOU KNOW?

1. Since Detroit is one of the NHL's Original Six franchises, it's only natural they have strong rivalries against the other five teams. Their playoff records against those teams as of 2020 stood at: Boston Bruins 3-5; Chicago Blackhawks 7-9; Montreal Canadiens 7-5; New York Rangers 4-1; Toronto Maple Leafs 11-12.

2. Detroit has met Toronto 23 times in the playoffs and the Maple Leafs hold a 12-11 edge. At the end of the 2019-20 campaign, Toronto also had the edge in overall regular-season and postseason showdowns at 351-345-93. The Red Wings haven't had much luck in the Stanley Cup Final against the Leafs, either, as their record stands at 1-6, including six consecutive series defeats.

3. The Red Wings made playoff history in 1941-42 by becoming the first and only team to blow a 3-0 lead in games in a Stanley Cup Final. It was also the first final in league history to be decided in seven games. The seventh game, which was held at Maple Leaf Gardens, was also the first time a crowd of over 16,000 had attended an NHL game in Canada.

4. The most preferred opponent for the Red Wings is the Minnesota Wild as Detroit owns a 63.1 winning percentage against the club in all play followed by Anaheim at 61.6 percent. The teams they have the most

difficulty with are the Montreal Canadiens, with a 43.7 winning percentage, and the Philadelphia Flyers, with a 44.9 winning percentage.

5. When it comes to all-time goals for and against, the Red Wings have the most luck against the Arizona Coyotes and Winnipeg Jets. Detroit has scored an average of 3.6 goals per game against the Jets and 3.5 against the Coyotes. On the other side of the coin, they struggle with the Philadelphia Flyers as they have allowed 3.5 goals against per game on average.

6. There has been a lot of animosity between the Red Wings and Colorado Avalanche due to an incident in the 1996 playoffs. Colorado's Claude Lemieux drove Kris Draper's face into the boards and the injury required reconstructive surgery. When the teams met in Detroit in March the following year, the game featured nine fights and a brawl and was nicknamed "Fight Night at the Joe." The teams were involved in three more brawls in the following 13 months.

7. The cities of Detroit and Chicago are separated by about 280 miles of highway, which has resulted in an intense rivalry. Both franchises joined the NHL in 1926-27, and the teams had met 820 times, including the playoffs, by the end of the 2019-20 season. Detroit held the overall lead at 369-271-84-15 but Chicago had a 43-38 postseason edge.

8. One of the newer rivalries Detroit has developed has been with the Tampa Bay Lightning. Tampa eliminated Detroit

from the playoffs in 2015 and 2016, and the Wings haven't made the playoffs since. Fights between the squads are commonplace and Hall-of-Famer Steve Yzerman, who spent his entire playing career with the Red Wings, left his post as Tampa's general manager to take over the same position in Detroit in 2019. In addition, Tampa tied Detroit's NHL regular-season win record of 62 in 2018-19.

9. The St. Louis Blues have been a thorn in Detroit's side for many years. Detroit downed St. Louis in five games in the 1988 Norris Division Final, but the Blues beat the Wings in seven games in 1991 after Detroit held a 3-1 lead in games. The clubs met three straight seasons in the playoffs from 1996 through 1998, with Detroit winning every series. The Red Wings came back from a 3-2 deficit in games in 1996 and won Game 7 in double overtime. They have also won five of the seven series against St. Louis.

10. The Red Wings have been relatively successful against Pacific Division teams in the postseason. Their playoff series records against these clubs stand at: Anaheim Ducks 4-2; Arizona Coyotes 4-0; Calgary Flames 2-1; Edmonton Oilers 0-3; Los Angeles Kings 1-1; San Jose Sharks 2-3; Vancouver Canucks 1-0, for a total of 14-10. The Wings have yet to meet the Las Vegas Golden Knights.

CHAPTER 15:

THE AWARDS SECTION

QUIZ TIME!

1. How many times have the Red Wings won the Prince of Wales Trophy?

    a. 13
    b. 14
    c. 12
    d. 8

2. How many members of the Red Wings' organization have been awarded the Lester Patrick Trophy?

    a. 11
    b. 19
    c. 30
    d. 24

3. Nicklas Lidström and Henrik Zetterberg have won the Lady Byng Trophy three times each.

    a. True
    b. False

4. How many times did Gordie Howe win the Art Ross Trophy?

    a. 5

    b. 3

    c. 6

    d. 7

5. Who was the first Red Wing goalie to win the Vezina Trophy?

    a. Johnny Mowers

    b. Normie Smith

    c. Terry Sawchuk

    d. Harry Lumley

6. Who did not attend the first NHL All-Star Game in 1947?

    a. Ted Lindsay

    b. Roy Conacher

    c. Bill Quackenbush

    d. Jack Stewart

7. Sid Abel named head coach for how many All-Star games?

    a. 5

    b. 3

    c. 6

    d. 4

8. Pavel Datsyuk won the Frank J. Selke Trophy three seasons in a row.

    a. True

    b. False

9. How many NHL awards did Henrik Zetterberg win?

    a. One

    b. Four

    c. Three

    d. Two

10. Who won the Conn Smythe Trophy for the 1997-98 playoffs?

    a. Chris Osgood

    b. Steve Yzerman

    c. Nicklas Lidström

    d. Brendan Shanahan

11. The Lester B. Pearson Award was renamed the Ted Lindsay Award in 2010.

    a. True

    b. False

12. Who won the Mark Messier Leadership Award in 2006-07?

    a. Todd Bertuzzi

    b. Tomas Holmström

    c. Chris Chelios

    d. Henrik Zetterberg

13. Who was the lone Red Wing to make the 1990-91 All-Rookie Team?

    a. Bob Wilkie

    b. Yves Racine

    c. Keith Primeau

    d. Sergei Fedorov

14. The Red Wings won four President's Trophies in the 2000s.

    a. True
    b. False

15. Who won back-to-back Jack Adams Awards in 1986-87 and 1987-88?

    a. Nick Polano
    b. Scotty Bowman
    c. Jacques Demers
    d. Bryan Murray

16. What award did Carl Voss win in 1932-33?

    a. Lady Byng Memorial Trophy
    b. Calder Memorial Trophy
    c. Hart Memorial Trophy
    d. Art Ross Trophy

17. Which player won the James Norris Memorial Trophy in 1953-54?

    a. Al Arbour
    b. Red Kelly
    c. Marcel Pronovost
    d. Bob Goldham

18. Vladimir Konstantinov won the NHL Plus-Minus Award with what rating?

    a. + 57
    b. + 59
    c. + 60
    d. + 64

19. Who won the Foundation Player Award in 2002-03?

    a. Brett Hull

    b. Luc Robitaille

    c. Steve Yzerman

    d. Darren McCarty

20. In 1955, 20 Red Wings attended the All-Star Game.

    a. True

    b. False

QUIZ ANSWERS

1. A – 13

2. D – 24

3. B - False

4. C – 6

5. B – Normie Smith

6. B – Roy Conacher

7. D – 4

8. A – True

9. C – 3

10. B – Steve Yzerman

11. A – True

12. C – Chris Chelios

13. D – Sergei Fedorov

14. A – True

15. C – Jacques Demers

16. B – Calder Memorial Trophy

17. B – Red Kelly

18. C – + 60

19. D – Darren McCarty

20. A – True

DID YOU KNOW?

1. As a franchise and individually, the Red Wings have won numerous NHL trophies. Here's a list: Stanley Cup (11), Clarence S. Campbell Bowl (6), Prince of Wales Trophy (13), Presidents' Trophy (6), Art Ross Trophy (7), Bill Masterton Memorial Trophy (2), Calder Memorial Trophy (5), Conn Smythe Trophy (5), Frank J. Selke Trophy (7), Hart Memorial Trophy (9), Jack Adams Award (4), James Norris Memorial Trophy (9), King Clancy Memorial Trophy (2), Lady Byng Memorial Trophy(14), Ted Lindsay Award(2), Vezina Trophy (5) and William M. Jennings Trophy (2).

2. The Art Ross Trophy for the NHL's leading scorer has been won by Ted Lindsay and Gordie Howe. Lindsay led the league in 1949-50 with Howe taking over for the next four consecutive seasons. Howe also won it in 1956-57 and 1962-63.

3. Detroit has had five rookies win the Calder Trophy as the league's best first-year player. Carl Voss took the honor in 1932-33, followed by fellow forward Jim McFadden in 1947-48. The other three were captured by goaltenders Terry Sawchuk in 1950-51, Glenn Hall in 1955-56 and Roger Crozier in 1964-65.

4. The playoff MVP is awarded the Conn Smythe Trophy. Five Red Wings have had their name engraved on it. They

are goaltenders Roger Crozier in 1965-66 and Mike Vernon in 1996-97; forward Steve Yzerman in 1997-98; blue-liner Nicklas Lidström in 2001-02; and forward Henrik Zetterberg in 2007-08.

5. Four Red Wings have won the Frank Selke Trophy as the NHL's top defensive forward. Sergei Fedorov won it in 1993-94 and 1995-96, Steve Yzerman in 1999-2000, Kris Draper in 2003-04, and Pavel Datsyuk won it three seasons in a row, from 2008 through 2010.

6. The Hart Trophy is viewed as one of the most prestigious because it's awarded to the most valuable player to his team during the regular season. Ebbie Goodfellow was the first Detroit player to win it in 1939-40 and Sid Abel followed in 1948-49. Gordie Howe won it for 1951-52, 1952-53, 1956-57, 1957-58, 1959-60 and 1962-63. The last Red Wing to win it was Sergei Fedorov in 1993-94.

7. Nicklas Lidström certainly was one of the NHL's greatest defensemen as he won seven James Norris Trophies as the league's top blue-liners. He won it three seasons in a row from 2001 through 2003 and another three consecutive years from 2006 through 2008. He won his last Norris in 2010-11. Red Kelly, who also played center during his career, was the first Detroit rearguard to win it in 1953-54 and Paul Coffey was awarded it for 1994-95.

8. Several Red Wings have won the Lady Byng Trophy for sportsmanship, ability, and gentlemanly conduct. Marty Barry won it first in 1936-37 and was followed by Bill

Quackenbush (1948-49), Red Kelly (1950-51, 1952-53, 1953-54), Earl Reibel (1955-56), Alex Delvecchio (1958-59, 1965-66, 1968-69), Marcel Dionne (1974-75). Finally, Pavel Datsyuk tied an NHL record by winning it four years in a row, from 2006 through 2009.

9. The Vezina Trophy is awarded to the NHL's top goaltender for the season while the William M. Jennings Trophy is given to the goaltenders on the team that allows the fewest goals against during the regular season. The Vezina was won by Normie Smith in 1936-37, Johnny Mowers in 1942-43, and Terry Sawchuk in 1951-52, 1952-53 and 1954-55. Chris Osgood and Mike Vernon shared the Jennings Trophy in 1995-96 and Osgood shared it with Dominik Hasek in 2007-08.

10. A total of 81 former Red Wing players, coaches and officials have been inducted into the Hockey Hall of Fame. This includes 61 enshrined as players and 14 in the builders' category. In addition, 24 members of the franchise have received the Lester Patrick Trophy. This award was born in 1966 and is presented by the NHL and USA Hockey to honor those who have greatly contributed to ice hockey in the USA.

CONCLUSION

There you have it. From front to back and start to finish, you've just read the newest trivia and fact book on the Detroit Red Wings. You've just gone through nearly a century's worth of information and statistics on your favorite hockey team.

We trust you enjoyed reading it and we hope you learned something new or re-lived some great and not-so-great memories of the team while doing so.

Most Red Wings' fans may already know the majority of facts and trivia written about the club. They typically know the history of the franchise as well as all the scoop on its most famous players, coaches and general managers. However, maybe something caught your eye that you did not know before.

It's impossible to list every single piece of information and statistic for this storied franchise, so we hope you'll forgive us if we've missed your favorite player, coach or bit of Red Wing trivia. There's enough information here to challenge your fellow fans with though to see who's the ultimate Red Wing fan. You can also add some of your own trivia when challenging others if it's not included here.

The book can also be used to convert fans of other NHL clubs and to teach youngsters about America's most successful NHL franchise.

The Red Wings have set several league records since joining the NHL. And, even though their 25 consecutive seasons in the playoffs is only the third-longest streak in the league, it may never be equaled again.

Every hockey team has its ups and downs, and the Red Wings are no exception. They may be enduring some hard times at the moment, but with loyal fans like you, the club is bound to turn things around soon.

Made in United States
Orlando, FL
13 October 2023

37869407R00080